FIRST PAST THE POST®

11+ COMPREHENSIONS

Book 1

CLASSIC LITERATURE

Tests 1 - 10

How to use this pack to make the most of 11 plus exam preparation

It is important to remember that for 11 plus exams there is no national syllabus, no pass mark and no retake option! It is therefore vitally important that your child is fully primed to perform to the best of their ability so that they give themselves the best possible chance on the day.

Unlike similar publications, the **First Past The Post®** series uniquely assesses your child's performance on a question-by-question basis, helping to identify areas for improvement and providing suggestions for further targeted tests.

English Comprehension

This collection of tests is representative of the standard comprehension section of contemporary multi-discipline 11 plus exams, including those set by CEM (Durham University). Each test contains a variety of question styles that are common across grammar and independent school exams. Typically, questions test the student's ability to extract factual information, draw inferences, and use their own judgement or reasoning skills in order to interpret the extract. In addition, some questions test the student's knowledge of vocabulary, grammar and literary techniques. The suggested time for each test is based on data obtained from conventional classroom testing sessions.

Never has it been more useful to learn from mistakes!

Students can improve by as much as 15% not only by focused practice but also by targeting any weak areas.

How to manage your child's practice

To get the most up-to-date information, visit the Eleven Plus Exams website (www.elevenplusexams.co.uk). Eleven Plus Exams is the largest UK online resource with over 40,000 webpages and a forum administered by a select group of experienced moderators.

About the authors

The Eleven Plus Exams' **First Past The Post®** series has been created by a team of experienced tutors and authors from leading British universities including Oxford and Cambridge.

Published by University of Buckingham Press

With special thanks to the children who tested our material at the Eleven Plus Exams centre in Harrow.

ISBN: 9781908684295

Contents Page

This workbook comprises ten comprehensions made up of 15 questions each, and each should take 12 minutes to complete.

Once you have completed the tests, mark them using the answers given and upload your scores onto our 11+ Peer-Compare™ System to see how well you have performed in comparison to others who have taken these tests.

You can register by visiting www.elevenplusexams.co.uk/firstpastthepost to post your results anonymously and obtain feedback.

Instructions

For each question, mark your answer by drawing a firm horizontal line in the box next to your chosen option on the question sheet:

1. This is an example question.

- ⬭ a. Wrong answer
- ⬭ b. Wrong answer
- ⬭ c. Wrong answer
- ▬ d. Right answer
- ⬭ e. Wrong answer

Use the method suggested below for working through comprehension papers:

i. Always **read through the extract first**, you should not go straight to the questions.

ii. **Do not skim-read,** your first reading should be sufficiently thorough so that you have a good understanding of the passage and can answer the questions more quickly and accurately. Otherwise, you are unlikely to have sufficient time available.

iii. You should **underline key information** (e.g. names of characters, places, dates, events or key words that provide an explanation of the subject matter) as this will help you to navigate the passage and recall the main points, especially where the question does not provide line references. Be careful not to let the underlining slow down your reading or distract you from understanding what you are reading.

iv. Read the questions and then **refer back to the text** in order to find the relevant answers. If you underlined key words and read thoroughly, then you should be able to easily find the relevant parts of the passage that you need to refer back in order to find the answer.

v. There are broadly **four main types of question** as shown in the table opposite. Remember, some questions might be a combination of these different types.

To mark your papers, use the 'Answers' section at the back of this booklet. The mark scheme will give you the correct answer option, as well as a short explanation of how each question should have been worked out.

For content-based questions, line references are provided pointing you to the location of the answer in the text.

For other types of questions, the mark scheme states whether inference, judgement or knowledge was required to arrive at the right answer.

Where relevant, line references are also provided for inference and judgement questions to indicate where the text hints at the answer.

Comprehension questions fall into four main types, as shown in the table below:

Type	Where/how to find the answer	Example(s)
Factual content	Specifically stated in the text	Given a text that explains 'When Sophie was 11, she had a terrible accident', you might be asked how old Sophie was at the time of her accident. The answer will be specifically stated in the text.
Logical inference	Not directly stated in the text, but can be inferred (understood) from the details given	Given a text that describes the setting as 'cold, snowy and dark', you might be asked what season it is in the story or to identify true/false statements. You must use the hints given in the passage to work out the most likely answer.
Personal judgement	Not directly stated in the text; you must read more deeply into the text to form your own opinion	You may be asked to describe the feelings or reactions of a character or about the intentions of the author (e.g. What was Tommy's mood on his first day at school?). You must read between the lines and look at the language and tone used to form your own opinion.
Knowledge of grammar, vocabulary and literary techniques	Not stated in the text at all; you must use your knowledge to answer the question	Questions may ask about word meanings or ask you to recognise literary techniques such as alliteration and onomatopoeia. Be careful with vocabulary questions - all answers options may provide a correct definition of a word, but only one will fit the context of the passage.

BLANK PAGE

FIRST PAST THE POST® SERIES

Comprehensions

Alice in Wonderland (Test 1)

Marking Grid																
Question	1	2	3	4	5	6	7	8	9	10	11	12	13	14	15	Total
✓ or ✗																

Read the following instructions carefully:

1. You have 12 minutes to complete this test of 15 questions.

2. You are recommended to spend 5 minutes reading the text, and 7 minutes answering the questions.

3. Work as quickly and as carefully as you can.

4. When you have finished a page, continue straight on to the next page. Do not waste time.

5. You can write on the text itself, or use the available space on the question paper to do any working. However, only mark your final answer in the answer boxes.

6. Mark your answer using a pencil, by drawing a firm horizontal line in the box next to your chosen option.

7. To change an answer, rub out your original answer completely and then mark on your new choice.

8. If you cannot answer a question, go on to the next question.

9. When you have completed the paper, use the time remaining to go back to any questions you have missed out and check your answers.

Good luck!

After you have finished this paper you can use the 11+ Peer-Compare System™ to see how well you have performed compared to others who have taken this test. You can register by visiting www.elevenplusexams.co.uk/firstpastthepost to post your results anonymously and obtain feedback.

An extract from 'Alice in Wonderland'
by Lewis Carroll

ALICE was beginning to get very tired of sitting by her sister on the bank, and of having nothing to do. Once or twice she had peeped into the book her sister was reading, but it had no pictures or conversations in it, "and what is the use of a book," thought Alice, "without pictures or conversations?"

5 So she was considering in her own mind (as well as she could, for the day made her feel very sleepy and stupid), whether the pleasure of making a daisy-chain would be worth the trouble of getting up and picking the daisies, when suddenly a White Rabbit with pink eyes ran close by her.

There was nothing so very remarkable in that, nor did Alice think it so very 10 much out of the way to hear the Rabbit say to itself, "Oh dear! Oh dear! I shall be too late!" But when the Rabbit actually took a watch out of its waistcoat-pocket and looked at it and then hurried on, Alice started to her feet, for it flashed across her mind that she had never before seen a rabbit with either a waistcoat-pocket, or a watch to take out of it, and, burning with curiosity, she 15 ran across the field after it and was just in time to see it pop down a large rabbit-hole, under the hedge. In another moment, down went Alice after it!

The rabbit-hole went straight on like a tunnel for some way and then dipped suddenly down, so suddenly that Alice had not a moment to think about stopping herself before she found herself falling down what seemed to be a 20 very deep well.

Either the well was very deep, or she fell very slowly, for she had plenty of time, as she went down, to look about her. First, she tried to make out what she was coming to, but it was too dark to see anything; then she looked at the sides of the well and noticed that they were filled with cupboards and book-25 shelves; here and there she saw maps and pictures hung upon pegs. She took down a jar from one of the shelves as she passed. It was labelled "ORANGE MARMALADE," but, to her great disappointment, it was empty; she did not like to drop the jar, so managed to put it into one of the cupboards as she fell past it.

30 Down, down, down! Would the fall never come to an end? There was nothing else to do, so Alice soon began talking to herself. "Dinah'll miss me very much to-night, I should think!" (Dinah was the cat.) "I hope they'll remember her saucer of milk at tea-time. Dinah, my dear, I wish you were down here with me!" Alice felt that she was dozing off, when suddenly, thump! thump! down 35 she came upon a heap of sticks and dry leaves, and the fall was over.

Alice was not a bit hurt, and she jumped up in a moment. She looked up, but it was all dark overhead; before her was another long passage and the White Rabbit was still in sight, hurrying down it. There was not a moment to be lost. Away went Alice like the wind and was just in time to hear it say, as it turned a

40 corner, "Oh, my ears and whiskers, how late it's getting!" She was close behind it when she turned the corner, but the Rabbit was no longer to be seen.

She found herself in a long, low hall, which was lit up by a row of lamps hanging from the roof. There were doors all 'round the hall, but they were all locked; and when Alice had been all the way down one side and up the other,

45 trying every door, she walked sadly down the middle, wondering how she was ever to get out again.

Suddenly she came upon a little table, all made of solid glass. There was nothing on it but a tiny golden key, and Alice's first idea was that this might belong to one of the doors of the hall; but, alas! either the locks were too

50 large, or the key was too small, but, at any rate, it would not open any of them. However, on the second time 'round, she came upon a low curtain she had not noticed before, and behind it was a little door about fifteen inches high. She tried the little golden key in the lock, and to her great delight, it fitted!

55 Alice opened the door and found that it led into a small passage, not much larger than a rat-hole; she knelt down and looked along the passage into the loveliest garden you ever saw. How she longed to get out of that dark hall and wander about among those beds of bright flowers and those cool fountains, but she could not even get her head through the doorway. "Oh," said Alice,

60 "how I wish I could shut up like a telescope! I think I could, if I only knew how to begin." Alice went back to the table, half hoping she might find another key on it, or at any rate, a book of rules for shutting people up like telescopes. This time she found a little bottle on it ("which certainly was not here before," said Alice), and tied 'round the neck of the bottle was a paper label, with the words

65 "DRINK ME" beautifully printed on it in large letters.

"No, I'll look first," she said, "and see whether it's marked 'poison' or not," for she had never forgotten that, if you drink from a bottle marked "poison," it is almost certain to disagree with you, sooner or later. However, this bottle was not marked "poison," so Alice ventured to taste it, and, finding it very nice (it

70 had a sort of mixed flavour of cherry-tart, custard, pineapple, roast turkey, toffee and hot buttered toast), she very soon finished it off.

"What a curious feeling!" said Alice. "I must be shutting up like a telescope!" And so it was indeed! She was now only ten inches high, and her face

brightened up at the thought that she was now the right size for going through
75 the little door into that lovely garden.

After a while, finding that nothing more happened, she decided on going into the garden at once; but, alas for poor Alice! When she got to the door, she found she had forgotten the little golden key, and when she went back to the table for it, she found she could not possibly reach it: she could see it quite
80 plainly through the glass and she tried her best to climb up one of the legs of the table, but it was too slippery, and when she had tired herself out with trying, the poor little thing sat down and cried.

"Come, there's no use in crying like that!" said Alice to herself rather sharply. "I advise you to leave off this minute!" She generally gave herself very good
85 advice (though she very seldom followed it), and sometimes she scolded herself so severely as to bring tears into her eyes. Soon her eye fell on a little glass box that was lying under the table: she opened it and found in it a very small cake, on which the words "EAT ME" were beautifully marked in currants. "Well, I'll eat it," said Alice, "and if it makes me grow larger, I can reach the
90 key; and if it makes me grow smaller, I can creep under the door: so either way I'll get into the garden, and I don't care which happens!"

She ate a little bit and said anxiously to herself, "Which way? Which way?" holding her hand on the top of her head to feel which way she was growing; and she was quite surprised to find that she remained the same size. So she
95 set to work and very soon finished off the cake.

1. Why is Alice bored when sitting on the bank?
   - a. She hates her sister.
   - b. She has seen a white rabbit.
   - c. She has a short attention span.
   - d. She has nothing to do.
   - e. She is always bored.

2. Why isn't Alice interested in reading her sister's book?
   - a. It has no pictures or conversations.
   - b. It's about a topic which Alice would find boring.
   - c. Alice has read the book before.
   - d. Alice's sister never shares anything with her.
   - e. Alice can't read.

3. In lines 10-12 the White Rabbit begins to talk and looks at his watch. Choose the option which best describes that passage.
   - a. frightening
   - b. boring
   - c. humorous
   - d. sad
   - e. none of the above

4. Which two of the following best describes the well that Alice fell into?
   1. short
   2. long
   3. magical
   4. dirty
   - a. 1 and 2
   - b. 2 and 3
   - c. 1 and 3
   - d. 1 and 4
   - e. 3 and 4

5. Why is Alice disappointed that the 'ORANGE MARMALADE' jar is empty?
   - a. She was hoping to give it to her sister as a gift.
   - b. She would have liked to try some of it.
   - c. She wanted to smash it.
   - d. She only went into the tunnel to find some food.
   - e. Orange is her favourite colour.

6. 'Would the fall never come to an end?' (line 30).
   Which one of the following words is a verb in this sentence?

   ⬭ a. fall
   ⬭ b. never
   ⬭ c. end
   ⬭ d. come
   ⬭ e. the

7. 'Alice felt that she was dozing off, when suddenly, thump! thump! down
   she came...' (lines 34-35)
   What is 'thump' is an example of?

   ⬭ a. onomatopoeia
   ⬭ b. an adjective
   ⬭ c. a metaphor
   ⬭ d. a phrase
   ⬭ e. a description

8. How does Alice feel as she is falling down the well?
   ⬭ a. scared because she doesn't know where the well might end
   ⬭ b. concerned that she might hurt herself
   ⬭ c. hungry
   ⬭ d. happy to begin an adventure
   ⬭ e. bored as it was taking so long

9. Why does Alice keep chasing the White Rabbit?
   ⬭ a. He is running late.
   ⬭ b. Alice is running late.
   ⬭ c. She is curious about him.
   ⬭ d. Alice is running away from her sister.
   ⬭ e. The rabbit told Alice to follow him.

10. Why doesn't the golden key open the doors?
   ⬭ a. It is made of glass.
   ⬭ b. The doors can only be opened by a silver key.
   ⬭ c. There is a curtain in the way of the keyhole.
   ⬭ d. It is the wrong size.
   ⬭ e. Alice doesn't try hard enough.

11. '"What a curious feeling!" said Alice. "I must be shutting up like a telescope!"' (line 72)
    To whom is Alice speaking at this point?

    ⬭ a. the narrator
    ⬭ b. the White Rabbit
    ⬭ c. her sister
    ⬭ d. the reader
    ⬭ e. herself

12. '...when she had tired herself out with trying, the poor little thing sat down and cried.' (lines 81-82)
    How is the reader supposed to feel towards Alice at this point?

    ⬭ a. impatient
    ⬭ b. indifferent
    ⬭ c. critical
    ⬭ d. sympathetic
    ⬭ e. grateful

13. Which of these is the best definition for 'seldom' in line 85?

    ⬭ a. always
    ⬭ b. mostly
    ⬭ c. reluctantly
    ⬭ d. never
    ⬭ e. not often

14. Why does Alice only eat a small amount of the cake unlike drinking all of the liquid in the bottle at once?

    ⬭ a. She doesn't like cake.
    ⬭ b. She enjoyed the flavours in the bottle more.
    ⬭ c. She has learned to be more cautious.
    ⬭ d. She is concentrating on the garden.
    ⬭ e. The cake looks more suspicious than the bottle.

15. What age do you imagine Alice to be?

    ⬭ a. 0-5 years-old
    ⬭ b. 6-13 years-old
    ⬭ c. 14-21 years-old
    ⬭ d. 22-40 years-old
    ⬭ e. 41 years-old or older

BLANK PAGE

Comprehensions

A Little Princess (Test 2)

Marking Grid																
Question	1	2	3	4	5	6	7	8	9	10	11	12	13	14	15	Total
✓ or ✗																

Read the following instructions carefully:

1. You have 12 minutes to complete this test of 15 questions.

2. You are recommended to spend 5 minutes reading the text, and 7 minutes answering the questions.

3. Work as quickly and as carefully as you can.

4. When you have finished a page, continue straight on to the next page. Do not waste time.

5. You can write on the text itself, or use the available space on the question paper to do any working. However, only mark your final answer in the answer boxes.

6. Mark your answer using a pencil, by drawing a firm horizontal line in the box next to your chosen option.

7. To change an answer, rub out your original answer completely and then mark on your new choice.

8. If you cannot answer a question, go on to the next question.

9. When you have completed the paper, use the time remaining to go back to any questions you have missed out and check your answers.

Good luck!

After you have finished this paper you can use the 11+ Peer-Compare System™ to see how well you have performed compared to others who have taken this test. You can register by visiting www.elevenplusexams.co.uk/firstpastthepost to post your results anonymously and obtain feedback.

An extract from 'A Little Princess'
by Frances Hodgson Burnett

ONCE on a dark winter's day, when the yellow fog hung so thick and heavy in the streets of London that the lamps were lighted and the shop windows blazed with gas as they do at night, an odd-looking little girl sat in a cab with her father and was driven rather slowly through the big thoroughfares.

5 She sat with her feet tucked under her, and leaned against her father, who held her in his arm, as she stared out of the window at the passing people with a queer old-fashioned thoughtfulness in her big eyes.

She was such a little girl that one did not expect to see such a look on her small face. It would have been an old look for a child of twelve, and Sara Crewe was
10 only seven. The fact was, however, that she was always dreaming and thinking odd things and could not herself remember any time when she had not been thinking things about grown-up people and the world they belonged to. She felt as if she had lived a long, long time.

At this moment she was remembering the voyage she had just made from
15 Bombay with her father, Captain Crewe. She was thinking of the big ship, of the Lascars passing silently to and fro on it, of the children playing about on the hot deck, and of some young officers' wives who used to try to make her talk to them and laugh at the things she said.

Principally, she was thinking of what a queer thing it was that at one time one
20 was in India in the blazing sun, and then in the middle of the ocean, and then driving in a strange vehicle through strange streets where the day was as dark as the night. She found this so puzzling that she moved closer to her father.

"Papa," she said in a low, mysterious little voice which was almost a whisper, "papa."

25 "What is it, darling?" Captain Crewe answered, holding her closer and looking down into her face. "What is Sara thinking of?"

"Is this the place?" Sara whispered, cuddling still closer to him. "Is it, papa?"

"Yes, little Sara, it is. We have reached it at last." And though she was only seven years old, she knew that he felt sad when he said it.

30 It seemed to her many years since he had begun to prepare her mind for "the place," as she always called it. Her mother had died when she was born, so she had never known or missed her. Her young, handsome, rich, petting father

seemed to be the only relation she had in the world. They had always played together and been fond of each other. She only knew he was rich because she had heard people say so when they thought she was not listening, and she had also heard them say that when she grew up she would be rich, too. She did not know all that being rich meant. She had always lived in a beautiful bungalow, and had been used to seeing many servants who made salaams to her and called her "Missee Sahib," and gave her her own way in everything. She had had toys and pets and an ayah who worshipped her, and she had gradually learned that people who were rich had these things. That, however, was all she knew about it.

During her short life only one thing had troubled her, and that thing was "the place" she was to be taken to someday. The climate of India was very bad for children, and as soon as possible they were sent away from it—generally to England and to school. She had seen other children go away, and had heard their fathers and mothers talk about the letters they received from them. She had known that she would be obliged to go also, and though sometimes her father's stories of the voyage and the new country had attracted her, she had been troubled by the thought that he could not stay with her.

"Couldn't you go to that place with me, papa?" she had asked when she was five years old. "Couldn't you go to school, too? I would help you with your lessons."

"But you will not have to stay for a very long time, little Sara," he had always said. "You will go to a nice house where there will be a lot of little girls, and you will play together, and I will send you plenty of books, and you will grow so fast that it will seem scarcely a year before you are big enough and clever enough to come back and take care of papa."

She had liked to think of that. To keep the house for her father; to ride with him, and sit at the head of his table when he had dinner-parties; to talk to him and read his books—that would be what she would like most in the world, and if one must go away to "the place" in England to attain it, she must make up her mind to go. She did not care very much for other little girls, but if she had plenty of books she could console herself. She liked books more than anything else, and was, in fact, always inventing stories of beautiful things and telling them to herself. Sometimes she had told them to her father, and he had liked them as much as she did.

"Well, papa," she said softly, "if we are here I suppose we must be resigned."

He laughed at her old-fashioned speech and kissed her. He was really not at all
70 resigned himself, though he knew he must keep that a secret. His quaint little
Sara had been a great companion to him, and he felt he should be a lonely
fellow when, on his return to India, he went into his bungalow knowing he
need not expect to see the small figure in its white frock come forward to
meet him. So he held her very closely in his arm as the cab rolled into the big,
75 dull square in which stood the house which was their destination.

1. What atmosphere is created by the description of the weather?

- a. light-hearted
- b. gloomy
- c. quizzical
- d. romantic
- e. uncomfortable

2. Where does this passage take place?

- a. Chicago
- b. India
- c. France
- d. London
- e. Bombay

3. Which of these is the best synonym for 'blazed' in line 3?

- a. shone
- b. smiled
- c. cooled
- d. fought
- e. broken

4. What can you tell about the relationship between father and daughter based on the way they were sitting?

- a. They felt uncomfortable.
- b. They loved each other.
- c. They despised each other.
- d. They were annoyed at each other.
- e. They were indifferent to one another.

5. Which of these is true?

- a. The girl behaved immaturely.
- b. The girl was an orphan.
- c. The girl was obnoxious.
- d. The girl felt older than her age.
- e. The girl was very unhappy.

6. 'She was thinking of the big ship...' (line 15)
   Which of these words is an adjective?

   ⬭ a. big
   ⬭ b. ship
   ⬭ c. was
   ⬭ d. she
   ⬭ e. thinking

7. Why did the girl move closer to her father?

   ⬭ a. She did not trust him.
   ⬭ b. She was keen to become friends.
   ⬭ c. She was puzzled.
   ⬭ d. She was doing a puzzle.
   ⬭ e. He smelt nice.

8. Which of these best describes the way Sara said "Papa" (line 23)?

   ⬭ a. boisterously
   ⬭ b. quietly
   ⬭ c. politely
   ⬭ d. suspiciously
   ⬭ e. loudly

9. How old was Sara?

   ⬭ a. five
   ⬭ b. twelve
   ⬭ c. seven
   ⬭ d. nine
   ⬭ e. sixteen

10. How did Sara feel about her mother?

   ⬭ a. She preferred her mother to her father.
   ⬭ b. She envied her.
   ⬭ c. She did not know her.
   ⬭ d. She missed her.
   ⬭ e. She knew her well.

11. How did Sara feel about 'the place' (lines 30-31)?

    ⬭ a. The thought of it troubled her.

    ⬭ b. She was happy because her father would go with her.

    ⬭ c. She was enthusiastic about going there.

    ⬭ d. The thought of it made her cry.

    ⬭ e. The thought of it made her smile.

12. Why did Sara think she was being sent away from India?

    ⬭ a. She was rich .

    ⬭ b. The climate was bad for children.

    ⬭ c. She did not have many friends.

    ⬭ d. There were no good schools there.

    ⬭ e. She was badly behaved.

13. What was Sara most looking forward to at school?

    ⬭ a. making new friends

    ⬭ b. playing with the other girls

    ⬭ c. the weather in London

    ⬭ d. being away from her father

    ⬭ e. reading books

14. How did Sara's father feel about being separated from her?

    ⬭ a. excited

    ⬭ b. fearful

    ⬭ c. relieved

    ⬭ d. melancholy

    ⬭ e. grateful

15. 'A Little Princess'

    What type of phrase is this?

    ⬭ a. a metaphor

    ⬭ b. a proverb

    ⬭ c. a title

    ⬭ d. a simile

    ⬭ e. a catchphrase

BLANK PAGE

FIRST PAST THE POST® SERIES

Comprehensions

A Modern Cinderella (Test 3)

Marking Grid																
Question	1	2	3	4	5	6	7	8	9	10	11	12	13	14	15	Total
✓ or ✗																

Read the following instructions carefully:

1. You have 12 minutes to complete this test of 15 questions.

2. You are recommended to spend 5 minutes reading the text, and 7 minutes answering the questions.

3. Work as quickly and as carefully as you can.

4. When you have finished a page, continue straight on to the next page. Do not waste time.

5. You can write on the text itself, or use the available space on the question paper to do any working. However, only mark your final answer in the answer boxes.

6. Mark your answer using a pencil, by drawing a firm horizontal line in the box next to your chosen option.

7. To change an answer, rub out your original answer completely and then mark on your new choice.

8. If you cannot answer a question, go on to the next question.

9. When you have completed the paper, use the time remaining to go back to any questions you have missed out and check your answers.

Good luck!

After you have finished this paper you can use the 11+ Peer-Compare System™ to see how well you have performed compared to others who have taken this test. You can register by visiting www.elevenplusexams.co.uk/firstpastthepost to post your results anonymously and obtain feedback.

An extract from 'A Modern Cinderella'
by Amanda M. Douglas

AMONG green New England hills stood an ancient house, many-gabled, mossy-roofed, and quaintly built, but picturesque and pleasant to the eye; for a brook ran babbling through the orchard that encompassed it about, a garden-plat stretched upward to the whispering birches on the slope, and
5 patriarchal elms stood sentinel upon the lawn, as they had stood almost a century ago, when the Revolution rolled that way and found them young.

One summer morning, when the air was full of country sounds, of mowers in the meadow, black-birds by the brook, and upon the hill-side the old house wore its cheeriest aspect, and a certain humble history began.

10 "Nan!"

"Yes, Di."

And a head, brown-locked, blue-eyed, soft-featured, looked in at the open door in answer to the call.

"Just bring me the third volume of 'Wilhelm Meister,' there's a dear. It's
15 hardly worthwhile to rouse such a restless ghost as I, when I'm once fairly laid."

As she spoke, Di pulled up her black braids, thumped the pillow of the couch where she was lying, and with eager eyes went down the last page of her book.

20 "Nan!"

"Yes, Laura," replied the girl, coming back with the third volume for the literary cormorant, who took it with a nod, still too content upon the "Confessions of a Fair Saint" to remember the failings of a certain plain sinner.

25 "Don't forget the Italian cream for dinner. I depend upon it; for it's the only thing fit for me this hot weather."

And Laura, the cool blonde, disposed the folds of her white gown more gracefully about her, and touched up the eyebrow of the Minerva she was drawing.

30 "Little daughter!"

"Yes, father."

"Let me have plenty of clean collars in my bag, for I must go at once; and some of you bring me a glass of cider in about an hour;—I shall be in the lower garden."

35 The old man went away into his imaginary paradise, and Nan into that domestic purgatory on a summer day,—the kitchen. There were vines about the windows, sunshine on the floor, and order everywhere; but it was haunted by a cooking-stove, that family altar whence such varied incense rises to appease the appetite of household gods, before which such dire
40 incantations are pronounced to ease the wrath and woe of the priestess of the fire, and about which often linger saddest memories of wasted temper, time, and toil.

Nan was tired, having risen with the birds,—hurried, having many cares those happy little housewives never know,—and disappointed in a hope that
45 hourly "dwindled, peaked, and pined." She was too young to make the anxious lines upon her forehead seem at home there, too patient to be burdened with the labor others should have shared, too light of heart to be pent up when earth and sky were keeping a blithe holiday. But she was one of that meek sisterhood who, thinking humbly of themselves, believe they
50 are honored by being spent in the service of less conscientious souls, whose careless thanks seem quite reward enough.

To and fro she went, silent and diligent, giving the grace of willingness to every humble or distasteful task the day had brought her; but some malignant sprite seemed to have taken possession of her kingdom, for
55 rebellion broke out everywhere. The kettles would boil over most obstreperously,—the mutton refused to cook with the meek alacrity to be expected from the nature of a sheep,—the stove, with unnecessary warmth of temper, would glow like a fiery furnace,—the irons would scorch,—the linens would dry,—and spirits would fail, though patience never.

60 Nan tugged on, growing hotter and wearier, more hurried and more hopeless, till at last the crisis came; for in one fell moment she tore her gown, burnt her hand, and smutched the collar she was preparing to finish in the most unexceptionable style. Then, if she had been a nervous woman, she would have scolded; being a gentle girl, she only "lifted up her voice and
65 wept."

"Behold, she watereth her linen with salt tears, and bewaileth herself because of much tribulation. But, lo! Help cometh from afar: a strong man bringeth lettuce wherewith to stay her, plucketh berries to comfort her withal, and clasheth cymbals that she may dance for joy."

70 The voice came from the porch, and, with her hope fulfilled, Nan looked up to greet John Lord, the house-friend, who stood there with a basket on his arm; and as she saw his honest eyes, kind lips, and helpful hands, the girl thought this plain young man the comeliest, most welcome sight she had beheld that day.

75 "How good of you, to come through all this heat, and not to laugh at my despair!" she said, looking up like a grateful child, as she led him in.

1. Where do the events of the story take place?
   - ⬭ a. England
   - ⬭ b. New England
   - ⬭ c. Old England
   - ⬭ d. Scotland
   - ⬭ e. New York

2. Which of the following is the best definition for the word picturesque' (line 2)?
   - ⬭ a. depressing and dreary
   - ⬭ b. attractive but smelly
   - ⬭ c. dark and small
   - ⬭ d. aesthetically ideal
   - ⬭ e. anomalous

3. Which two statements are true about the setting?
   1. A brook runs through the orchard.
   2. A brook surrounds the orchard.
   3. A brook runs parallel to the orchard.
   4. The orchard surrounds a brook.
   - ⬭ a. 1 and 2
   - ⬭ b. 2 and 4
   - ⬭ c. 1 and 3
   - ⬭ d. 1 and 4
   - ⬭ e. 2 and 3

4. When do the events of this story take place?
   - ⬭ a. September
   - ⬭ b. spring
   - ⬭ c. summer
   - ⬭ d. autumn
   - ⬭ e. June

5. What opinion is the reader expected to form of Nan, from the description of her appearance?
   - ⬭ a. She is likeable.
   - ⬭ b. She is untrustworthy.
   - ⬭ c. She is ill-tempered.
   - ⬭ d. She is funny.
   - ⬭ e. She is heroic.

6. Why does Laura say that Italian cream is the only thing fit for her dinner?

    ⬭ a. Italian cream is best served hot.
    ⬭ b. She is lactose intolerant.
    ⬭ c. It is too hot to eat anything else.
    ⬭ d. It is too cold to eat anything else.
    ⬭ e. Her cream has to be from Italy.

7. 'The old man went away into his imaginary paradise...' (line 35)
   Which of the following words is a verb?

    ⬭ a. away
    ⬭ b. old
    ⬭ c. went
    ⬭ d. man
    ⬭ e. imaginary

8. Which of the following words is the best antonym for the word 'domestic' (line 36)?

    ⬭ a. parallel
    ⬭ b. unintentional
    ⬭ c. foreign
    ⬭ d. dome
    ⬭ e. household

9. Which of the following words best describes Nan?

    ⬭ a. selfish
    ⬭ b. impatient
    ⬭ c. flirtatious
    ⬭ d. funny
    ⬭ e. patient

10. What is the problem with the kitchen?

    ⬭ a. It is always messy and problem-filled.
    ⬭ b. It is too small to work in.
    ⬭ c. It is too dark.
    ⬭ d. It smells of rotting vegetables.
    ⬭ e. It is so clean that there is often nothing for Nan to do.

11. Which literary technique is prominent in the following phrase:
'...the stove... would glow like a fiery furnace' (lines 57-58)?

- a. personification
- b. simile
- c. metaphor
- d. catchphrase
- e. proverb

12. Why does Nan grow wearier?

- a. She is hot and overworked.
- b. She is hot and underworked.
- c. She is lazy.
- d. She spends some time outside playing.
- e. She is preparing a feast for the village.

13. What is the main message in John Lord's speech that begins "Behold, she watereth her linen..." (lines 66-69)?

- a. Lettuce is a key ingredient.
- b. Never wash linen.
- c. Friends can help.
- d. Dancing makes people happy.
- e. There was no message.

14. How does Nan feel about John Lord?

- a. She doesn't know him.
- b. She is grateful to see him.
- c. She does not trust him.
- d. She does not like him.
- e. She is afraid of him.

15. Who is the main character in this story?

- a. John Lord
- b. Father
- c. Di
- d. Laura
- e. Nan

BLANK PAGE

FIRST PAST THE POST® SERIES

Comprehensions

Black Beauty (Test 4)

Marking Grid															
Question	1	2	3	4	5	6	7	8	9	10	11	12	13	14	15	Total
✓ or ✗															

Read the following instructions carefully:

1. You have 12 minutes to complete this test of 15 questions.

2. You are recommended to spend 5 minutes reading the text, and 7 minutes answering the questions.

3. Work as quickly and as carefully as you can.

4. When you have finished a page, continue straight on to the next page. Do not waste time.

5. You can write on the text itself, or use the available space on the question paper to do any working. However, only mark your final answer in the answer boxes.

6. Mark your answer using a pencil, by drawing a firm horizontal line in the box next to your chosen option.

7. To change an answer, rub out your original answer completely and then mark on your new choice.

8. If you cannot answer a question, go on to the next question.

9. When you have completed the paper, use the time remaining to go back to any questions you have missed out and check your answers.

Good luck!

After you have finished this paper you can use the 11+ Peer-Compare System™ to see how well you have performed compared to others who have taken this test. You can register by visiting www.elevenplusexams.co.uk/firstpastthepost to post your results anonymously and obtain feedback.

An extract from 'Black Beauty'
by Anna Sewell

THE first place that I can well remember was a large pleasant meadow with a pond of clear water in it. Some shady trees leaned over it, and rushes and water-lilies grew at the deep end. Over the hedge on one side we looked into a ploughed field, and on the other we looked over a gate at our master's house,

5 which stood by the roadside; at the top of the meadow was a grove of fir trees, and at the bottom a running brook overhung by a steep bank.

While I was young I lived upon my mother's milk, as I could not eat grass. In the daytime I ran by her side, and at night I lay down close by her. When it was hot we used to stand by the pond in the shade of the trees, and when it was

10 cold we had a nice warm shed near the grove.

As soon as I was old enough to eat grass my mother used to go out to work in the daytime, and come back in the evening.

There were six young colts in the meadow besides me; they were older than I was; some were nearly as large as grown-up horses. I used to run with them,

15 and had great fun; we used to gallop all together round and round the field as hard as we could go. Sometimes we had rather rough play, for they would frequently bite and kick as well as gallop.

One day, when there was a good deal of kicking, my mother whinnied to me to come to her, and then she said:

20 "I wish you to pay attention to what I am going to say to you. The colts who live here are very good colts, but they are cart-horse colts, and of course they have not learned manners. You have been well-bred and well-born; your father has a great name in these parts, and your grandfather won the cup two years at the Newmarket races; your grandmother had the sweetest temper of

25 any horse I ever knew, and I think you have never seen me kick or bite. I hope you will grow up gentle and good, and never learn bad ways; do your work with a good will, lift your feet up well when you trot, and never bite or kick even in play."

I have never forgotten my mother's advice; I knew she was a wise old horse,

30 and our master thought a great deal of her. Her name was Duchess, but he often called her Pet.

Our master was a good, kind man. He gave us good food, good lodging, and kind words; he spoke as kindly to us as he did to his little children. We were all fond of him, and my mother loved him very much. When she saw him at the gate she would neigh with joy, and trot up to him. He would pat and stroke her and say, "Well, old Pet, and how is your little Darkie?" I was a dull black, so he called me Darkie; then he would give me a piece of bread, which was very good, and sometimes he brought a carrot for my mother. All the horses would come to him, but I think we were his favourites. My mother always took him to the town on a market day in a light gig.

There was a plowboy, Richard, who sometimes came into our field to pluck blackberries from the hedge. When he had eaten all he wanted he would have what he called fun with the colts, throwing stones and sticks at them to make them gallop. We did not much mind him, for we could gallop off; but sometimes a stone would hit and hurt us.

One day he was at this game, and did not know that the master was in the next field; but he was there, watching what was going on; over the hedge he jumped in a snap, and catching Richard by the arm, he gave him such a box on the ear as made him roar with the pain and surprise. As soon as we saw the master we trotted up nearer to see what went on.

"Bad boy!" he said, "bad boy! to chase the colts. This is not the first time, nor the second, but it shall be the last. There—take your money and go home; I shall not want you on my farm again." So we never saw Richard any more. Old Daniel, the man who looked after the horses, was just as gentle as our master, so we were well off.

Before I was two years old a circumstance happened which I have never forgotten. It was early in the spring; there had been a little frost in the night, and a light mist still hung over the woods and meadows. I and the other colts were feeding at the lower part of the field when we heard, quite in the distance, what sounded like the cry of dogs. The oldest of the colts raised his head, pricked his ears, and said, "There are the hounds!" and immediately cantered off, followed by the rest of us to the upper part of the field, where we could look over the hedge and see several fields beyond. My mother and an old riding horse of our master's were also standing near, and seemed to know all about it.

"They have found a hare," said my mother, "and if they come this way we shall see the hunt."

And soon the dogs were all tearing down the field of young wheat next to ours. I never heard such a noise as they made. They did not bark, nor howl, nor whine, but kept on a "yo! yo, o, o! yo! yo, o, o!" at the top of their voices. After

them came a number of men on horseback, some of them in green coats, all galloping as fast as they could. The old horse snorted and looked eagerly after them, and we young colts wanted to be galloping with them, but they were soon away into the fields lower down; here it seemed as if they had come to a
75 stand; the dogs left off barking, and ran about every way with their noses to the ground.

"They have lost the scent," said the old horse; "perhaps the hare will get off."

"What hare?" I said.

"Oh! I don't know what hare; likely enough it may be one of our own hares out
80 of the woods; any hare they can find will do for the dogs and men to run after;" and before long the dogs began their "yo! yo, o, o!" again, and back they came altogether at full speed, making straight for our meadow at the part where the high bank and hedge overhang the brook.

1. What is the first place the narrator can remember?
   - a. a ship
   - b. an orchard
   - c. a meadow
   - d. a field
   - e. a garden

2. Who or what is the narrator?
   - a. a child
   - b. an adult
   - c. a horse
   - d. a ghost
   - e. an author

3. How did the narrator feel about his mother?
   - a. They were strangers.
   - b. He disliked her.
   - c. He found her overbearing.
   - d. They were close.
   - e. He didn't mind her.

4. What is a 'colt' (line 13)?
   - a. a child
   - b. a black horse
   - c. a race horse
   - d. a young male horse
   - e. an older friend

5. Why did the colts bite and kick when they galloped?
   - a. They were rude.
   - b. They disliked each other.
   - c. They disliked the speaker.
   - d. They got out of hand.
   - e. They were playing.

6. What did his mother tell the narrator about the colts?

    ⬭ a. He should be their friend.
    ⬭ b. He should kick and bite them.
    ⬭ c. He is different to them.
    ⬭ d. He is better looking than them.
    ⬭ e. He should learn from their manners.

7. Why did Duchess' master often call her 'Pet' (line 31)?

    ⬭ a. He called all his animals 'Pet'.
    ⬭ b. He treated her like a house pet.
    ⬭ c. He disliked her.
    ⬭ d. He was being affectionate.
    ⬭ e. He was trying to make the others jealous.

8. 'My mother always took him to the town on a market day in a light gig.' (lines 39-40)

What does this sentence imply about how his mother felt towards the master?

    ⬭ a. She was fond of him and enjoyed pleasing him.
    ⬭ b. She was impatient with him.
    ⬭ c. She found it a burden to take him to the market.
    ⬭ d. She found him unfair and wished to irritate him.
    ⬭ e. She would trot very lightly.

9. What do you think the narrator feels about Richard?

    ⬭ a. He thought Richard was annoying.
    ⬭ b. He thought Richard was fun to play with.
    ⬭ c. He wished Richard would be his friend.
    ⬭ d. He was frightened of Richard.
    ⬭ e. He loved Richard.

10. Why did the master give Richard 'such a box on the ear' (lines 48-49)?

    ⬭ a. He hated him.
    ⬭ b. He missed him.
    ⬭ c. He was angry with him.
    ⬭ d. He was shocked to see him.
    ⬭ e. He was happy with him.

11. What atmosphere is created by the description of the weather on the spring morning?

- a. It creates suspense.
- b. It creates a sense of horror.
- c. It makes the reader laugh.
- d. It makes the reader confused.
- e. It creates a sense of boredom.

12. What do you think happens next in the story?

- a. The horses forget about the dogs.
- b. The horses get involved in the hunt.
- c. The dogs give up their chase.
- d. The dogs chase the hare into the horses' field.
- e. The master chases the horses.

13. Which of the following best characterises the ending?

- a. exciting and scary
- b. a happy ending
- c. exciting and unresolved
- d. comical and unusual
- e. depressing and resolved

14. What type of narration is used in the passage?

- a. 1st person without opinions
- b. 1st person with opinions
- c. 3rd person without opinions
- d. 3rd person with opinions
- e. There is no narration.

15. Who are the intended readers of this story?

- a. infants
- b. children
- c. teenagers
- d. adults
- e. the elderly

BLANK PAGE

Comprehensions

Five Children and It (Test 5)

Marking Grid															
Question	1	2	3	4	5	6	7	8	9	10	11	12	13	14	15	Total
✓ or ✗																

Read the following instructions carefully:

1. You have 12 minutes to complete this test of 15 questions.

2. You are recommended to spend 5 minutes reading the text, and 7 minutes answering the questions.

3. Work as quickly and as carefully as you can.

4. When you have finished a page, continue straight on to the next page. Do not waste time.

5. You can write on the text itself, or use the available space on the question paper to do any working. However, only mark your final answer in the answer boxes.

6. Mark your answer using a pencil, by drawing a firm horizontal line in the box next to your chosen option.

7. To change an answer, rub out your original answer completely and then mark on your new choice.

8. If you cannot answer a question, go on to the next question.

9. When you have completed the paper, use the time remaining to go back to any questions you have missed out and check your answers.

Good luck!

After you have finished this paper you can use the 11+ Peer-Compare System™ to see how well you have performed compared to others who have taken this test. You can register by visiting www.elevenplusexams.co.uk/firstpastthepost to post your results anonymously and obtain feedback.

An extract from 'Five Children and It'
by Edith Nesbit

THE house was three miles from the station, but before the dusty hired fly had rattled along for five minutes the children began to put their heads out of the carriage window and to say, "Aren't we nearly there?" And every time they passed a house, which was not very often, they all said, "Oh, is THIS it?" But it

5   never was, till they reached the very top of the hill, just past the chalk-quarry and before you come to the gravel-pit. And then there was a white house with a green garden and an orchard beyond, and mother said, "Here we are!"

"How white the house is," said Robert.

"And look at the roses," said Anthea.

10 "And the plums," said Jane.

"It is rather decent," Cyril admitted.

The Baby said, "Wanty go walky" and the fly stopped with a last rattle and jolt.

Everyone got its legs kicked or its feet trodden on in the scramble to get out of the carriage that very minute, but no one seemed to mind. Mother, curiously

15 enough, was in no hurry to get out; and even when she had come down slowly and by the step, and with no jump at all, she seemed to wish to see the boxes carried in, and even to pay the driver, instead of joining in that first glorious rush round the garden and the orchard and the thorny, thistly, briery, brambly wilderness beyond the broken gate and the dry fountain at the side of the

20 house. But the children were wiser, for once. It was not really a pretty house at all; it was quite ordinary, and mother thought it was rather inconvenient, and was quite annoyed at there being no shelves, to speak of, and hardly a cupboard in the place. Father used to say that the ironwork on the roof and coping was like an architect's nightmare. But the house was deep in the

25 country, with no other house in sight, and the children had been in London for two years, without so much as once going to the seaside even for a day by an excursion train, and so the White House seemed to them a sort of Fairy Palace set down in an Earthly Paradise. For London is like prison for children, especially if their relations are not rich.

30 Of course there are the shops and the theatres, and Maskelyne and Cook's, and things, but if your people are rather poor you don't get taken to the theatres, and you can't buy things out of the shops; and London has none of those nice things that children may play with without hurting the things or themselves - such as trees and sand and woods and waters. And nearly

35 everything in London is the wrong sort of shape - all straight lines and flat streets, instead of being all sorts of odd shapes, like things are in the country. Trees are all different, as you know, and I am sure some tiresome person must have told you that there are no two blades of grass exactly alike. But in streets, where the blades of grass don't grow, everything is like everything else. This is

40 why so many children who live in towns are so extremely naughty. They do not know what is the matter with them, and no more do their fathers and mothers, aunts, uncles, cousins, tutors, governesses, and nurses; but I know. And so do you now. Children in the country are naughty sometimes, too, but that is for quite different reasons.

45 The children had explored the gardens and the outhouses thoroughly before they were caught and cleaned for tea, and they saw quite well that they were certain to be happy at the White House. They thought so from the first moment, but when they found the back of the house covered with jasmine, an in white flower, and smelling like a bottle of the most expensive scent that is

50 ever given for a birthday present; and when they had seen the lawn, all green and smooth, and quite different from the brown grass in the gardens at Camden Town; and when they had found the stable with a loft over it and some old hay still left, they were almost certain; and when Robert had found the broken swing and tumbled out of it and got a lump on his head the size of

55 an egg, and Cyril had nipped his finger in the door of a hutch that seemed made to keep rabbits in, if you ever had any, they had no longer any doubts whatever.

The best part of it all was that there were no rules about not going to places and not doing things. In London almost everything is labelled 'You mustn't

60 touch,' and though the label is invisible, it's just as bad, because you know it's there, or if you don't you jolly soon get told.

The White House was on the edge of a hill, with a wood behind it - and the chalk-quarry on one side and the gravel-pit on the other. Down at the bottom of the hill was a level plain, with queer-shaped white buildings where people

65 burnt lime, and a big red brewery and other houses; and when the big chimneys were smoking and the sun was setting, the valley looked as if it was filled with golden mist, and the limekilns and oat-houses glimmered and glittered till they were like an enchanted city out of the Arabian Nights.

1. What is a 'fly' (line 1)?
- a. a sledge
- b. a van
- c. a horse and carriage
- d. a taxi
- e. a rickshaw

2. When the children said, "Aren't we nearly there?" in line 3, how were they feeling?
- a. restless
- b. sad
- c. passive
- d. frightened
- e. indifferent

3. Which of these best describes the location of the house?
- a. urban
- b. rural
- c. city
- d. jungle
- e. valley

4. What is an orchard?
- a. a place for feeding cattle
- b. a place ware wood is stored
- c. the home of grizzly bears
- d. a place where cider is made
- e. a place where apples are grown

5. Which of the following best describes the Mother's behaviour on arrival at the house?
- a. She was the most excited.
- b. She was the least excited.
- c. She ran towards the house.
- d. She did not care about the boxes.
- e. She waited inside the house when the children arrived.

6. Why did the 'White House' seem like a 'Fairy Palace' to the children?

    1. They had not left London in a long time.

    2. It was in the countryside.

    3. It looked like London.

    4. Fairies lived there.

    ⬭ a. 1 and 2

    ⬭ b. 1 and 3

    ⬭ c. 2 and 3

    ⬭ d. 3 and 4

    ⬭ e. 1 and 4

7. According to the narrator, why is London 'like prison for children' (line 28)?

    ⬭ a. Londoners are rude to children.

    ⬭ b. There are no white houses.

    ⬭ c. There are hardly any children.

    ⬭ d. They are forced to go to school.

    ⬭ e. There is nothing for them to do.

8. Which of these opinions is expressed in the text?

    ⬭ a. Children from the country are never naughty.

    ⬭ b. Children from the country are the same as children from London.

    ⬭ c. Town and country children are both naughty but for different reasons.

    ⬭ d. Children from the town are the naughtiest.

    ⬭ e. Children from the country are always naughty.

9. Why did the children need to be 'cleaned for tea' (line 46)?

    ⬭ a. They were dirty from playing in the gardens.

    ⬭ b. They were dirty from the journey up.

    ⬭ c. Country children are smelly.

    ⬭ d. Guests were coming for tea.

    ⬭ e. Tea is an important ceremony.

10. '...smelling like a bottle of the most expensive scent...' (line 49)
    What type of phrase is this?

    ⬭ a. a metaphor

    ⬭ b. onomatopoeia

    ⬭ c. a question

    ⬭ d. a simile

    ⬭ e. a conjunction

11. How did Robert get a lump on his head?
- a. He fell from the roof.
- b. He got hit by the broken swing.
- c. His mother hit him.
- d. He fell from the broken swing.
- e. He had a bad headache.

12. How does the narrator imply the children feel about the rules in London?
- a. They like rules.
- b. They hate freedom.
- c. They dislike rules.
- d. They know they need boundaries.
- e. They think there aren't enough rules.

13. Why did the valley look 'as if it was filled with golden mist' (lines 66-67)?
- a. It was filled with smoke from the chimneys.
- b. It was snowing.
- c. There was spring pollen in the air.
- d. There were fairies in the valley.
- e. It was a mystery.

14. Which of the following is the best synonym for 'enchanted' in line 68?
- a. haunted
- b. magical
- c. vacant
- d. stunning
- e. depressing

15. From whose perspective is the passage written?
- a. the reader's
- b. the baby's
- c. mother's
- d. the children's
- e. the narrator's

FIRST PAST THE POST® SERIES

Comprehensions

How the Rhinoceros Got His Skin (Test 6)

Marking Grid															
Question	1	2	3	4	5	6	7	8	9	10	11	12	13	14	15	Total
✓ or ✗																

Read the following instructions carefully:

1. You have 12 minutes to complete this test of 15 questions.

2. You are recommended to spend 5 minutes reading the text, and 7 minutes answering the questions.

3. Work as quickly and as carefully as you can.

4. When you have finished a page, continue straight on to the next page. Do not waste time.

5. You can write on the text itself, or use the available space on the question paper to do any working. However, only mark your final answer in the answer boxes.

6. Mark your answer using a pencil, by drawing a firm horizontal line in the box next to your chosen option.

7. To change an answer, rub out your original answer completely and then mark on your new choice.

8. If you cannot answer a question, go on to the next question.

9. When you have completed the paper, use the time remaining to go back to any questions you have missed out and check your answers.

Good luck!

After you have finished this paper you can use the <u>11+ Peer-Compare System</u>™ to see how well you have performed compared to others who have taken this test. You can register by visiting <u>www.elevenplusexams.co.uk/firstpastthepost</u> to post your results anonymously and obtain feedback.

An extract from 'How the Rhinoceros Got His Skin' by Rudyard Kipling

ONCE upon a time, on an uninhabited island on the shores of the Red Sea, there lived a Man. And the Man lived by the Red Sea with nothing but his hat and his knife and a cooking-stove of the kind that you must particularly never touch. And one day he took flour and water and currants and plums and sugar

5 and things, and made himself one cake which was two feet across and three feet thick. It was indeed a Superior Comestible (that's magic), and he put it on stove because he was allowed to cook on the stove, and he baked it and he baked it till it was all done brown and smelt most sentimental. But just as he was going to eat it there came down to the beach from the Altogether

10 Uninhabited Interior one Rhinoceros with a horn on his nose, two piggy eyes, and few manners. In those days the Rhinoceros's skin fitted him quite tight. There were no wrinkles in it anywhere. He looked exactly like a Noah's Ark Rhinoceros, but of course much bigger. All the same, he had no manners then, and he has no manners now, and he never will have any manners. He said,

15 'How!' and the Man left that cake and climbed to the top of a palm tree with nothing on but his hat. And the Rhinoceros upset the oil-stove with his nose, and the cake rolled on the sand, and he spiked that cake on the horn of his nose, and he ate it, and he went away, waving his tail, to the desolate and Exclusively Uninhabited Interior which abuts on the islands of Mazanderan,

20 Socotra, and Promontories of the Larger Equinox. Then the Man came down from his palm-tree and put the stove on its legs and recited the following song, which, as you have not heard, I will now proceed to relate:—

Whosoever takes a cake
That a Man has baked
25 *Makes a dreadful mistake.*

And there was a great deal more in that than you would think.

Because, five weeks later, there was a heat wave in the Red Sea, and everybody took off all the clothes they had. The Man took off his hat; but the Rhinoceros took off his skin and carried it over his shoulder as he came down

30 to the beach to bathe. In those days it buttoned underneath with three buttons and looked like a waterproof. He said nothing whatever about the Man's cake, because he had eaten it all; and he never had any manners, then, since, or henceforward. He waddled straight into the water and blew bubbles through his nose, leaving his skin on the beach.

35 Presently the Man came by and found the skin, and he smiled one smile that ran all round his face two times. He rubbed his hands. Then he went to his

camp and filled his hat with cake-crumbs, for the Man never ate anything but cake, and never swept out his camp. He took that skin, and he shook that skin, and he scrubbed that skin, and he rubbed that skin just as full of old, dry, stale,
40 tickly cake-crumbs and some burned currants as ever it could possibly hold. Then he climbed to the top of his palm-tree and waited for the Rhinoceros to come out of the water and put it on.

And the Rhinoceros did. He buttoned it up with the three buttons, and it tickled like cake crumbs in bed. Then he wanted to scratch, but that made it
45 worse; and then he lay down on the sands and rolled and rolled and rolled, and every time he rolled the cake crumbs tickled him worse and worse and worse. Then he ran to the palm-tree and rubbed and rubbed and rubbed himself against it. He rubbed so much and so hard that he rubbed his skin into a great fold over his shoulders, and another fold underneath, where the
50 buttons used to be (but he rubbed the buttons off), and he rubbed some more folds over his legs. And it spoiled his temper, but it didn't make the least difference to the cake-crumbs. They were inside his skin and they tickled. So he went home, very angry indeed and horribly scratchy; and from that day to this every rhinoceros has great folds in his skin and a very bad temper, all on
55 account of the cake-crumbs inside.

But the Man came down from his palm-tree, wearing his hat, packed up his cooking-stove, and went away in the direction of Orotavo, Amygdala, the Upland Meadows of Anantarivo, and the Marshes of Sonaput.

1. Which of the following is the best antonym for 'uninhabited' in line 1?
   - a. forsaken
   - b. desolate
   - c. populated
   - d. plundered
   - e. untouched

2. Which two of the following items did the Man have with him?
   1. a scarf
   2. a bottle opener
   3. a hat
   4. a knife

   - a. 1 and 2
   - b. 1 and 3
   - c. 1 and 4
   - d. 2 and 3
   - e. 3 and 4

3. What was peculiar about the cake?
   - a. the ingredients
   - b. the colour
   - c. the proportion of fruit
   - d. the size
   - e. the smell

4. '...one Rhinoceros with a horn on his nose, two piggy eyes, and few manners.'
   (lines 10-11)
   Which of the following options best characterises this phrase?
   - a. alliterative
   - b. factual
   - c. ironic
   - d. descriptive
   - e. onomatopoeic

5. Why did the Man leave the cake?
   - a. He was not hungry. .
   - b. He was on a diet.
   - c. He wanted to share it with the Rhinoceros.
   - d. He enjoyed climbing trees.
   - e. He was afraid of the Rhinoceros.

6. How did the Rhinoceros feel after eating the Man's cake?
   1. unapologetic
   2. remorseful
   3. smug
   4. anxious

   - a. 1 and 2
   - b. 1 and 3
   - c. 2 and 3
   - d. 3 and 4
   - e. 1 and 4

7. Which of these is the best synonym for 'recited' in line 21?
   - a. recorded
   - b. concealed
   - c. applauded
   - d. decided
   - e. performed

8. Which of the following is the best definition for 'dreadful' in the context of line 25?
   - a. causing fear
   - b. idiotic
   - c. very serious
   - d. careless
   - e. without shame

9. Which of these best characterises the Man's song?
   - a. alliterative
   - b. metaphorical
   - c. informal
   - d. formal
   - e. rhyming

10. What was the main message behind the Man's song?
   - a. Rhinoceroses should not be trusted.
   - b. The Rhinoceros would regret his actions.
   - c. The Man would bake another cake.
   - d. The cake would make the Rhinoceros ill.
   - e. The Rhinoceros would shrink.

11. How did the Man feel when he found the Rhinoceros' skin?
   - a. ecstatic
   - b. remorseful
   - c. pensive
   - d. sceptical
   - e. brave

12. Why did the Rhinoceros fail to get rid of the cake-crumbs?
   - a. He could no longer take off his skin.
   - b. He did not know how to remove them.
   - c. He was not smart enough.
   - d. They were multiplying too quickly.
   - e. He did not know the cake-crumbs were there.

13. For which of the following were the cake-crumbs responsible for?
   - a. The Rhinoceros' bad temper and loose skin.
   - b. The Rhinoceros' good temper and grey skin.
   - c. The Rhinoceros' tight skin.
   - d. The Rhinoceros' tight and crumbly skin.
   - e. The Rhinoceros' thick skin and long horn.

14. Which of these statements is true?
   - a. The story is non-fictional.
   - b. The story is autobiographical.
   - c. The story is fictional.
   - d. The story would belong in a biology textbook.
   - e. The story is a advertisement.

15. Why are the words 'Man' and 'Rhinoceros' capitalised throughout the story?
   - a. It is a mistake.
   - b. They are the only names for them in the story.
   - c. Common nouns are always capitalised.
   - d. They are verbs.
   - e. They are titles.

FIRST PAST THE POST® SERIES

Comprehensions

Little Women (Test 7)

Marking Grid															
Question	1	2	3	4	5	6	7	8	9	10	11	12	13	14	15	Total
✓ or ✗																

Read the following instructions carefully:

1. You have 12 minutes to complete this test of 15 questions.

2. You are recommended to spend 5 minutes reading the text, and 7 minutes answering the questions.

3. Work as quickly and as carefully as you can.

4. When you have finished a page, continue straight on to the next page. Do not waste time.

5. You can write on the text itself, or use the available space on the question paper to do any working. However, only mark your final answer in the answer boxes.

6. Mark your answer using a pencil, by drawing a firm horizontal line in the box next to your chosen option.

7. To change an answer, rub out your original answer completely and then mark on your new choice.

8. If you cannot answer a question, go on to the next question.

9. When you have completed the paper, use the time remaining to go back to any questions you have missed out and check your answers.

Good luck!

After you have finished this paper you can use the 11+ Peer-Compare System™ to see how well you have performed compared to others who have taken this test. You can register by visiting www.elevenplusexams.co.uk/firstpastthepost to post your results anonymously and obtain feedback.

An extract from 'Little Women'
by Louise May Alcott

"CHRISTMAS won't be Christmas without any presents," grumbled Jo, lying on the rug.

"It's so dreadful to be poor!" sighed Meg, looking down at her old dress.

"I don't think it's fair for some girls to have plenty of pretty things, and other girls
5 nothing at all," added little Amy, with an injured sniff.

"We've got Father and Mother, and each other," said Beth contentedly from her corner.

The four young faces on which the firelight shone brightened at the cheerful words, but darkened again as Jo said sadly, "We haven't got Father, and shall not have him
10 for a long time." She didn't say "perhaps never," but each silently added it, thinking of Father far away, where the fighting was.

Nobody spoke for a minute; then Meg said in an altered tone, "You know the reason Mother proposed not having any presents this Christmas was because it is going to be a hard winter for everyone; and she thinks we ought not to spend
15 money for pleasure, when our men are suffering so in the army. We can't do much, but we can make our little sacrifices, and ought to do it gladly. But I am afraid I don't," and Meg shook her head, as she thought regretfully of all the pretty things she wanted.

"But I don't think the little we should spend would do any good. We've each got a
20 dollar, and the army wouldn't be much helped by our giving that. I agree not to expect anything from Mother or you, but I do want to buy *Undine and Sintran* for myself. I've wanted it so long," said Jo, who was a bookworm.

"I planned to spend mine in new music," said Beth, with a little sigh, which no one heard but the hearth brush and kettle-holder.

25 "I shall get a nice box of Faber's drawing pencils; I really need them," said Amy decidedly.

"Mother didn't say anything about our money, and she won't wish us to give up everything. Let's each buy what we want, and have a little fun; I'm sure we work hard enough to earn it," cried Jo, examining the heels of her shoes in a gentlemanly
30 manner.

"I know I do—teaching those tiresome children nearly all day, when I'm longing to enjoy myself at home," began Meg, in the complaining tone again.

"You don't have half such a hard time as I do," said Jo. "How would you like to be shut up for hours with a nervous, fussy old lady, who keeps you
35 trotting, is never satisfied, and worries you till you're ready to fly out the window or cry?"

"It's naughty to fret, but I do think washing dishes and keeping things tidy is the worst work in the world. It makes me cross, and my hands get so stiff, I can't practice well at all." And Beth looked at her rough hands with a sigh
40 that anyone could hear that time.

"I don't believe any of you suffer as I do," cried Amy, "for you don't have to go to school with impertinent girls, who plague you if you don't know your lessons, and laugh at your dresses, and label your father if he isn't rich, and insult you when your nose isn't nice."

45 "If you mean libel, I'd say so, and not talk about labels, as if Papa was a pickle bottle," advised Jo, laughing.

"I know what I mean, and you needn't be statirical about it. It's proper to use good words, and improve your vocabilary," returned Amy, with dignity.

"Don't peck at one another, children. Don't you wish we had the money
50 Papa lost when we were little, Jo? Dear me! How happy and good we'd be, if we had no worries!" said Meg, who could remember better times.

"You said the other day you thought we were a deal happier than the King children, for they were fighting and fretting all the time, in spite of their money."

55 "So I did, Beth. Well, I think we are. For though we do have to work, we make fun of ourselves, and are a pretty jolly set, as Jo would say."

"Jo does use such slang words!" observed Amy, with a reproving look at the long figure stretched on the rug.

Jo immediately sat up, put her hands in her pockets, and began to whistle.

60 "Don't, Jo. It's so boyish!"

"That's why I do it."

"I detest rude, unladylike girls!"

"I hate affected, niminy-piminy chits!"

"Birds in their little nests agree," sang Beth, the peacemaker, with such a funny
65 face that both sharp voices softened to a laugh, and the "pecking" ended for
that time.

1. At what time of year does the story begin?
   - a. summer
   - b. spring
   - c. autumn
   - d. winter
   - e. not possible to infer from the passage

2. Which of these best describes Jo, Meg and Amy's speech?
   - a. motivated
   - b. cautious
   - c. complaining
   - d. livid
   - e. petrified

3. Which of the sisters is the most contented?
   - a. Jo
   - b. Amy
   - c. Beth
   - d. Meg
   - e. None of them.

4. Why is the sisters' father away?
   - a. Their parents are separated.
   - b. He went away to earn more money.
   - c. He is angry with them.
   - d. He is a soldier.
   - e. He wanted to travel the world.

5. Which of the following is the best definition for 'regretfully' in the context of line 17?
   - a. sorrowfully
   - b. naively
   - c. dubiously
   - d. fortunately
   - e. unfortunately

6. Why aren't the sisters getting any presents this year?
   1. The family have run out of money.
   2. The sisters have been naughty.
   3. Presents can be easily sacrificed.
   4. To show respect for their soldiers.

   - a. 1 and 2
   - b. 1 and 3
   - c. 1 and 4
   - d. 2 and 3
   - e. 3 and 4

7. What is 'Undine and Sintran' most likely to be (line 21)?
   - a. a children's game
   - b. a doll
   - c. a special football
   - d. a chair
   - e. a book

8. Who is the youngest sister?
   - a. Amy
   - b. Beth
   - c. Meg
   - d. Jo
   - e. It is not possible to infer from the passage.

9. Which of the following is the best antonym for 'impertinent' in line 42?
   - a. rude
   - b. polite
   - c. intelligent
   - d. quirky
   - e. young

10. Which of the following is true?
   - a. The family was always poor.
   - b. The family was always rich.
   - c. The family was never happy.
   - d. The family used to be richer.
   - e. The family used to be poorer.

11. Amy gives Jo a 'reproving look' (line 57) What is meant by this?
- a. She looks at her enviously.
- b. She looks at her with a smile.
- c. She looks at her as if she wants to tell her off.
- d. She looks at her as if she wants to argue.
- e. She looks at her calmly.

12. Which of the following is the best description of Jo?
- a. She is a perfect example of what is meant by 'feminine'.
- b. She is obedient.
- c. She disregards the accepted definition of 'feminine'.
- d. She acts younger than her age.
- e. She is calm, quiet and polite.

13. What is the main focal point of the passage?
- a. the father
- b. the mother
- c. Christmastime
- d. the sisters and how they interact
- e. the presents

14. Which of the options best characterises the moral of the story?
- a. Shops should be closed at Christmas.
- b. Sisters should always fight.
- c. Mothers should buy Christmas presents for their children.
- d. Fathers should not leave their family.
- e. There was no moral.

15. What type of text does this passage come from?
- a. a textbook
- b. a newspaper
- c. a fictitious novel
- d. a magazine
- e. a science fiction novel

BLANK PAGE

FIRST PAST THE POST® SERIES

Comprehensions

Oliver Twist (Test 8)

Marking Grid

Question	1	2	3	4	5	6	7	8	9	10	11	12	13	14	15	Total
✓ or ✗																

Read the following instructions carefully:

1. You have 12 minutes to complete this test of 15 questions.

2. You are recommended to spend 5 minutes reading the text, and 7 minutes answering the questions.

3. Work as quickly and as carefully as you can.

4. When you have finished a page, continue straight on to the next page. Do not waste time.

5. You can write on the text itself, or use the available space on the question paper to do any working. However, only mark your final answer in the answer boxes.

6. Mark your answer using a pencil, by drawing a firm horizontal line in the box next to your chosen option.

7. To change an answer, rub out your original answer completely and then mark on your new choice.

8. If you cannot answer a question, go on to the next question.

9. When you have completed the paper, use the time remaining to go back to any questions you have missed out and check your answers.

Good luck!

After you have finished this paper you can use the 11+ Peer-Compare System™ to see how well you have performed compared to others who have taken this test. You can register by visiting www.elevenplusexams.co.uk/firstpastthepost to post your results anonymously and obtain feedback.

An extract from 'Oliver Twist'
by Charles Dickens

FOR the first six months after Oliver Twist was removed, the system was in full operation. It was rather expensive at first, in consequence of the increase in the undertaker's bill, and the necessity of taking in the clothes of all the paupers, which fluttered loosely on their wasted, shrunken forms, after a week
5 or two's gruel. But the number of workhouse inmates got thin as well as the paupers; and the board were in ecstasies.

The room in which the boys were fed, was a large stone hall, with a copper at one end: out of which the master, dressed in an apron for the purpose, and assisted by one or two women, ladled the gruel at mealtimes. Of this festive
10 composition each boy had one porringer, and no more—except on occasions of great public rejoicing, when he had two ounces and a quarter of bread besides.

The bowls never wanted washing. The boys polished them with their spoons till they shone again; and when they had performed this operation (which
15 never took very long, the spoons being nearly as large as the bowls), they would sit staring at the copper, with such eager eyes, as if they could have devoured the very bricks of which it was composed; employing themselves, meanwhile, in sucking their fingers most assiduously, with the view of catching up any stray splashes of gruel that might have been cast thereon. Boys have
20 generally excellent appetites. Oliver Twist and his companions suffered the tortures of slow starvation for three months: at last they got so voracious and wild with hunger, that one boy, who was tall for his age, and hadn't been used to that sort of thing (for his father had kept a small cook-shop), hinted darkly to his companions, that unless he had another basin of gruel per diem, he was
25 afraid he might some night happen to eat the boy who slept next him, who happened to be a weakly youth of tender age. He had a wild, hungry eye; and they implicitly believed him. A council was held; lots were cast who should walk up to the master after supper that evening, and ask for more; and it fell to Oliver Twist.

30 The evening arrived; the boys took their places. The master, in his cook's uniform, stationed himself at the copper; his pauper assistants ranged themselves behind him; the gruel was served out; and a long grace was said over the short commons. The gruel disappeared; the boys whispered each other, and winked at Oliver; while his next neighbours nudged him. Child as he
35 was, he was desperate with hunger, and reckless with misery. He rose from the table; and advancing to the master, basin and spoon in hand, said: somewhat alarmed at his own temerity:

"Please, sir, I want some more."

The master was a fat, healthy man; but he turned very pale. He gazed in
40 stupefied astonishment on the small rebel for some seconds, and then clung
for support to the copper. The assistants were paralysed with wonder; the
boys with fear.

"What!" said the master at length, in a faint voice.

"Please, sir," replied Oliver, "I want some more."

45 The master aimed a blow at Oliver's head with the ladle; pinioned him in his
arm; and shrieked aloud for the beadle.

The board were sitting in solemn conclave, when Mr. Bumble rushed into the
room in great excitement, and addressing the gentleman in the high chair,
said,

50 "Mr. Limbkins, I beg your pardon, sir! Oliver Twist has asked for more!"

There was a general start. Horror was depicted on every countenance.

"For more!" said Mr. Limbkins. "Compose yourself, Bumble, and answer me
distinctly. Do I understand that he asked for more, after he had eaten the
supper allotted by the dietary?"

55 "He did, sir," replied Bumble.

"That boy will be hung," said the gentleman in the white waistcoat. "I know
that boy will be hung."

Nobody controverted the prophetic gentleman's opinion. An animated
discussion took place. Oliver was ordered into instant confinement; and a bill
60 was next morning pasted on the outside of the gate, offering a reward of five
pounds to anybody who would take Oliver Twist off the hands of the parish. In
other words, five pounds and Oliver Twist were offered to any man or woman
who wanted an apprentice to any trade, business, or calling.

1. Why did the clothes of the paupers need to be taken in?
   - a. The seamstress had made a mistake.
   - b. The clothes were too big for the skinny children.
   - c. The children were fat and well-fed.
   - d. It was fashionable to wear tight clothes.
   - e. It was illegal to wear loose-fitting clothes.

2. How many people served the gruel?
   - a. one
   - b. five to six
   - c. two to three
   - d. one to two
   - e. none

3. How many bowls of gruel were the boys allowed?
   - a. as many as they liked
   - b. as many as the master felt like serving
   - c. four and above
   - d. none
   - e. only one

4. Why was there never any need to wash the bowls?
   - a. Every boy washed his own bowl.
   - b. None of the boys were served any gruel.
   - c. The bowls were self-cleaning.
   - d. Every morsel of gruel was eaten.
   - e. Nobody cared if the bowls were dirty.

5. Why did one boy joke that he might eat the boy sleeping next to him?
   - a. He did not like to eat gruel.
   - b. He was not used to being fed so little.
   - c. He was trying to diffuse the tension.
   - d. He wanted to frighten the other boys.
   - e. He often quarrelled with the boy who slept next to him.

6. The narrator mentions that 'a council was held' (line 27). What is meant by this?

    ⬭ a. The boys discussed how a solution could be found.
    ⬭ b. The boys formed an organisation to protect their rights.
    ⬭ c. Each boy literally held a council in their hands.
    ⬭ d. The boys discussed girls.
    ⬭ e. Every boy wrote down his feelings on the subject.

7. Which two things had to happen before the boys could eat?
    1. The master had to serve the gruel.
    2. Oliver had to steal the gruel.
    3. The boys had to play outside.
    4. A prayer was said.

    ⬭ a. 1 and 2
    ⬭ b. 1 and 3
    ⬭ c. 1 and 4
    ⬭ d. 2 and 3
    ⬭ e. 3 and 4

8. How did Oliver feel as he went up to ask for more?
    ⬭ a. excited to get another helping
    ⬭ b. proud that he had been braver than the other boys
    ⬭ c. stunned by his own bravery
    ⬭ d. mischievous for demanding more
    ⬭ e. unaware of his actions

9. Why did the master reply to Oliver in a faint voice?
    ⬭ a. He was a shy man.
    ⬭ b. He was a caring man.
    ⬭ c. He was shocked.
    ⬭ d. He did not wish to disturb the other boys.
    ⬭ e. He was trying to conceal his anger.

10. What was Oliver's punishment?
    ⬭ a. He was to be confined and then sold.
    ⬭ b. He was to be abandoned.
    ⬭ c. He was never allowed to eat again.
    ⬭ d. He was forbidden from sleeping in a bed.
    ⬭ e. He was shouted at.

11. Which two statements best explain the adults' reactions to Oliver's request?
   1. They were appalled by his disobedience.
   2. They only wanted to spend the bare minimum on feeding the boys.
   3. They were frightened that he would eat all of their food.
   4. They had never spoken to a child before.

   - a. 1 and 3
   - b. 2 and 3
   - c. 2 and 4
   - d. 3 and 4
   - e. 1 and 2

12. Which character does the author intend to be the reader's favourite?
   - a. Mr. Bumble
   - b. assistant number one
   - c. Mr. Limbkins
   - d. Oliver
   - e. the son of the cook-shop owner

13. Which of the following is the best antonym for 'consequence' in line 2?
   - a. effect
   - b. reaction
   - c. aftermath
   - d. cause
   - e. sequential

14. Which of the following is the best definition for 'stupefied' in line 40?
   - a. stupid and unintelligent
   - b. unable to think properly
   - c. excited and enthusiastic
   - d. able to move very quickly
   - e. content and calm

15. "Please, sir, I want some more." (line 38) What is this an example of?
   - a. a request
   - b. a demand
   - c. a title
   - d. a metaphor
   - e. a question

FIRST PAST THE POST® SERIES

Comprehensions

Peter Pan (Test 9)

Marking Grid															
Question	1	2	3	4	5	6	7	8	9	10	11	12	13	14	15	Total
✓ or ✗															

Read the following instructions carefully:

1. You have 12 minutes to complete this test of 15 questions.

2. You are recommended to spend 5 minutes reading the text, and 7 minutes answering the questions.

3. Work as quickly and as carefully as you can.

4. When you have finished a page, continue straight on to the next page. Do not waste time.

5. You can write on the text itself, or use the available space on the question paper to do any working. However, only mark your final answer in the answer boxes.

6. Mark your answer using a pencil, by drawing a firm horizontal line in the box next to your chosen option.

7. To change an answer, rub out your original answer completely and then mark on your new choice.

8. If you cannot answer a question, go on to the next question.

9. When you have completed the paper, use the time remaining to go back to any questions you have missed out and check your answers.

Good luck!

After you have finished this paper you can use the 11+ Peer-Compare System™ to see how well you have performed compared to others who have taken this test. You can register by visiting www.elevenplusexams.co.uk/firstpastthepost to post your results anonymously and obtain feedback.

An extract from 'Peter Pan'
by J. M. Barrie

FOR a moment after Mr. and Mrs. Darling left the house the night-lights by the beds of the three children continued to burn clearly. They were awfully nice little night-lights, and one cannot help wishing that they could have kept awake to see Peter; but Wendy's light blinked and gave such a yawn that the

5 other two yawned also, and before they could close their mouths all the three went out. There was another light in the room now, a thousand times brighter than the night-lights, and in the time we have taken to say this, it had been in all the drawers in the nursery, looking for Peter's shadow, rummaged the wardrobe and turned every pocket inside out. It was not really a light; it made

10 this light by flashing about so quickly, but when it came to rest for a second you saw it was a fairy, no longer than your hand, but still growing. It was a girl called Tinker Bell exquisitely gowned in a skeleton leaf, cut low and square, through which her figure could be seen to the best advantage.

A moment after the fairy's entrance the window was blown open by the

15 breathing of the little stars, and Peter dropped in. He had carried Tinker Bell part of the way, and his hand was still messy with the fairy dust.

"Tinker Bell," he called softly, after making sure that the children were asleep, "Tink, where are you?" She was in a jug for the moment, and liking it extremely; she had never been in a jug before.

20 "Oh, do come out of that jug, and tell me, do you know where they put my shadow?"

The loveliest tinkle as of golden bells answered him. It is the fairy language. You ordinary children can never hear it, but if you were to hear it you would know that you had heard it once before.

25 Tink said that the shadow was in the big box. She meant the chest of drawers, and Peter jumped at the drawers, scattering their contents to the floor with both hands, as kings toss ha'pence to the crowd. In a moment he had recovered his shadow, and in his delight he forgot that he had shut Tinker Bell up in the drawer.

30 If he thought at all, but I don't believe he ever thought, it was that he and his shadow, when brought near each other, would join like drops of water, and when they did not he was appalled. He tried to stick it on with soap from the

bathroom, but that also failed. A shudder passed through Peter, and he sat on the floor and cried.

35 His sobs woke Wendy, and she sat up in bed. She was not alarmed to see a stranger crying on the nursery floor; she was only pleasantly interested.

"Boy," she said courteously, "why are you crying?"

Peter could be exceeding polite also, having learned the grand manner at fairy ceremonies, and he rose and bowed to her beautifully. She was much pleased,
40 and bowed beautifully to him from the bed.

"What's your name?" he asked.

"Wendy Moira Angela Darling," she replied with some satisfaction. "What is your name?"

"Peter Pan."

45 She was already sure that he must be Peter, but it did seem a comparatively short name.

"Is that all?"

"Yes," he said rather sharply. He felt for the first time that it was a shortish name.

50 "I'm so sorry," said Wendy Moira Angela.

"It doesn't matter," Peter gulped.

She asked where he lived.

"Second to the right," said Peter, "and then straight on till morning."

"What a funny address!"

55 Peter had a sinking. For the first time he felt that perhaps it was a funny address.

"No, it isn't," he said.

"I mean," Wendy said nicely, remembering that she was hostess, "is that what they put on the letters?"

60 He wished she had not mentioned letters.

"Don't get any letters," he said contemptuously.

"But your mother gets letters?"

"Don't have a mother," he said. Not only had he no mother, but he had not the slightest desire to have one. He thought them very over-rated persons.
65 Wendy, however, felt at once that she was in the presence of a tragedy.

"O Peter, no wonder you were crying," she said, and got out of bed and ran to him.

"I wasn't crying about mothers," he said rather indignantly. "I was crying because I can't get my shadow to stick on. Besides, I wasn't crying."

70 "It has come off?"

"Yes."

Then Wendy saw the shadow on the floor, looking so draggled, and she was frightfully sorry for Peter. "How awful!" she said, but she could not help smiling when she saw that he had been trying to stick it on with soap. How
75 exactly like a boy!

Fortunately she knew at once what to do. "It must be sewn on," she said, just a little patronisingly.

"What's sewn?" he asked.

"You're dreadfully ignorant."

80 "No, I'm not."

But she was exulting in his ignorance. "I shall sew it on for you, my little man," she said, though he was tall as herself, and she got out her housewife [sewing bag], and sewed the shadow on to Peter's foot.

"I daresay it will hurt a little," she warned him.

85 "Oh, I shan't cry," said Peter, who was already of the opinion that he had never cried in his life.

1. Whose night-light started to go out first?
   - ⬭ a. Mr Darling's
   - ⬭ b. Mrs Darling's
   - ⬭ c. Wendy's
   - ⬭ d. Peter's
   - ⬭ e. Tinker Bell's

2. Which two of the following best explain why Peter's hand was messy?
   1. He had been carrying Tinker Bell.
   2. Tinker Bell was covered in fairy dust.
   3. Peter never washes his hands.
   4. His hands became dirty when he was looking for his shadow.

   - ⬭ a. 1 and 2
   - ⬭ b. 1 and 3
   - ⬭ c. 2 and 4
   - ⬭ d. 3 and 4
   - ⬭ e. 1 and 4

3. Why was Peter able to understand Tinker Bell?
   - ⬭ a. Peter is also a fairy.
   - ⬭ b. Tinker Bell spoke to Peter in English.
   - ⬭ c. Wendy translated the conversation for Peter.
   - ⬭ d. Tinker Bell used actions to help Peter understand her.
   - ⬭ e. Peter had heard the fairy language many times before.

4. Which of these best describes how Peter felt when he first found his shadow?
   - ⬭ a. dishevelled
   - ⬭ b. dignified
   - ⬭ c. triumphant
   - ⬭ d. cautious
   - ⬭ e. petrified

5. Why did Peter begin to cry?
   - ⬭ a. He did not know how to reattach his shadow.
   - ⬭ b. He had lost Tinker Bell.
   - ⬭ c. He was crying with happiness because he had found his shadow.
   - ⬭ d. He was lost.
   - ⬭ e. He was scared of Wendy.

6. Why was Wendy not alarmed to see a stranger in the nursery?

    ⬭ a. Strangers were always welcome in Wendy's nursery.
    ⬭ b. She was curious as to what he was doing there.
    ⬭ c. Peter had lived in the nursery before Wendy.
    ⬭ d. She was too tired to notice Peter's intrusion.
    ⬭ e. She found it funny that Peter was crying.

7. Which of the following is the best synonym for 'courteously' in line 37?

    ⬭ a. arrogantly
    ⬭ b. politely
    ⬭ c. bashfully
    ⬭ d. quietly
    ⬭ e. instinctively

8. When Wendy found out that the boy's name was Peter Pan, why did she ask "Is that all?" (line 47)?

    ⬭ a. She was not sure if he had finished speaking.
    ⬭ b. Boys usually have longer names than girls.
    ⬭ c. She was trying to be rude on purpose.
    ⬭ d. Peter was lying about his name.
    ⬭ e. She was surprised because his name was much shorter than hers.

9. How did Peter feel when Wendy laughed at his address?

    ⬭ a. indifferent
    ⬭ b. embarrassed
    ⬭ c. confused
    ⬭ d. repulsed
    ⬭ e. happy

10. Which of these is the best definition for 'hostess' in line 58?

    ⬭ a. someone who puts children to bed
    ⬭ b. a proactive young girl
    ⬭ c. someone without a mother
    ⬭ d. a woman who receives and entertains guests
    ⬭ e. someone whose house is broken into

11. How did Peter feel about mothers?

⬭ a. He missed his mother.
⬭ b. He felt like he had no need a mother.
⬭ c. He did not know what a mother was.
⬭ d. He was happy to talk about mothers because he loved the subject.
⬭ e. He would rather be talking about fathers.

12. "How awful!" (line 73) What is this an example of?

⬭ a. a question
⬭ b. a proverb
⬭ c. an exclamation
⬭ d. a title
⬭ e. a metaphor

13. Which two of these statements explain why Wendy called Peter "my little man" (line 81) even though he was as tall as her?
1. She was talking down to Peter.
2. She could not tell how tall he was.
3. Peter called Wendy "my little woman".
4. She was trying to act like a professional tailor.

⬭ a. 1 and 2
⬭ b. 1 and 4
⬭ c. 2 and 4
⬭ d. 2 and 3
⬭ e. 3 and 4

14. '"Oh, I shan't cry," said Peter, who was already of the opinion that he had never cried in his life.' (lines 85-86)
Which literary technique is the author using here to amuse the reader?

⬭ a. description, as Peter is described in a lot of detail
⬭ b. dehumanisation, as Peter is made to seem like an animal
⬭ c. exaggeration, as Peter's thoughts are exaggerated
⬭ d. simile, as Peter is being compared to something else
⬭ e. irony, as we know Peter has already cried at this point

15. What genre of book does this extract belong to?

⬭ a. fantasy
⬭ b. historical
⬭ c. romantic
⬭ d. science fiction
⬭ e. horror

BLANK PAGE

FIRST PAST THE POST® SERIES

Comprehensions

The Box of Robbers (Test 10)

Marking Grid																
Question	1	2	3	4	5	6	7	8	9	10	11	12	13	14	15	Total
✓ or ✗																

Read the following instructions carefully:

1. You have 12 minutes to complete this test of 15 questions.

2. You are recommended to spend 5 minutes reading the text, and 7 minutes answering the questions.

3. Work as quickly and as carefully as you can.

4. When you have finished a page, continue straight on to the next page. Do not waste time.

5. You can write on the text itself, or use the available space on the question paper to do any working. However, only mark your final answer in the answer boxes.

6. Mark your answer using a pencil, by drawing a firm horizontal line in the box next to your chosen option.

7. To change an answer, rub out your original answer completely and then mark on your new choice.

8. If you cannot answer a question, go on to the next question.

9. When you have completed the paper, use the time remaining to go back to any questions you have missed out and check your answers.

Good luck!

After you have finished this paper you can use the 11+ Peer-Compare System™ to see how well you have performed compared to others who have taken this test. You can register by visiting www.elevenplusexams.co.uk/firstpastthepost to post your results anonymously and obtain feedback.

An extract from 'The Box of Robbers'
by L. Frank Baum

NO one intended to leave Martha alone that afternoon, but it happened that everyone was called away, for one reason or another. Mrs. McFarland was attending the weekly card party held by the Women's Anti-Gambling League. Sister Nell's young man had called quite unexpectedly to take her
5 for a long drive. Papa was at the office, as usual. It was Mary Ann's day out. As for Emeline, she certainly should have stayed in the house and looked after the little girl; but Emeline had a restless nature.

"Would you mind, miss, if I just crossed the alley to speak a word to Mrs. Carleton's girl?" she asked Martha.

10 "'Course not," replied the child. "You'd better lock the back door, though, and take the key, for I shall be upstairs."

"Oh, I'll do that, of course, miss," said the delighted maid, and ran away to spend the afternoon with her friend, leaving Martha quite alone in the big house, and locked in, into the bargain.

15 The little girl read a few pages in her new book, sewed a few stitches in her embroidery and started to "play visiting" with her four favorite dolls. Then she remembered that in the attic was a doll's playhouse that hadn't been used for months, so she decided she would dust it and put it in order.

Filled with this idea, the girl climbed the winding stairs to the big room
20 under the roof. It was well lighted by three dormer windows and was warm and pleasant. Around the walls were rows of boxes and trunks, piles of old carpeting, pieces of damaged furniture, bundles of discarded clothing and other odds and ends of more or less value. Every well-regulated house has an attic of this sort, so I need not describe it.

25 The doll's house had been moved, but after a search Martha found it away over in a corner near the big chimney.

She drew it out and noticed that behind it was a black wooden chest which Uncle Walter had sent over from Italy years and years ago—before Martha was born, in fact. Mamma had told her about it one day; how there was no
30 key to it, because Uncle Walter wished it to remain unopened until he returned home; and how this wandering uncle, who was a mighty hunter, had gone into Africa to hunt elephants and had never been heard from afterwards.

The little girl looked at the chest curiously, now that it had by accident
35 attracted her attention.

It was quite big—bigger even than mamma's traveling trunk—and was studded
all over with tarnished brassheaded nails. It was heavy, too, for when Martha
tried to lift one end of it she found she could not stir it a bit. But there was a
place in the side of the cover for a key. She stooped to examine the lock, and
40 saw that it would take a rather big key to open it.

Then, as you may suspect, the little girl longed to open Uncle Walter's big box
and see what was in it. For we are all curious, and little girls are just as curious
as the rest of us.

"I don't b'lieve Uncle Walter'll ever come back," she thought. "Papa said once
45 that some elephant must have killed him. If I only had a key—" She stopped
and clapped her little hands together gayly as she remembered a big basket of
keys on the shelf in the linen closet. They were of all sorts and sizes; perhaps
one of them would unlock the mysterious chest!

She flew down the stairs, found the basket and returned with it to the attic.
50 Then she sat down before the brass-studded box and began trying one key
after another in the curious old lock. Some were too large, but most were too
small. One would go into the lock but would not turn; another stuck so fast
that she feared for a time that she would never get it out again. But at last,
when the basket was almost empty, an oddly-shaped, ancient brass key
55 slipped easily into the lock. With a cry of joy Martha turned the key with both
hands; then she heard a sharp "click," and the next moment the heavy lid flew
up of its own accord!

The little girl leaned over the edge of the chest an instant, and the sight that
met her eyes caused her to start back in amazement.

60 Slowly and carefully a man unpacked himself from the chest, stepped out upon
the floor, stretched his limbs and then took off his hat and bowed politely to
the astonished child.

He was tall and thin and his face seemed badly tanned or sunburnt.

Then another man emerged from the chest, yawning and rubbing his eyes like
65 a sleepy schoolboy. He was of middle size and his skin seemed as badly tanned
as that of the first.

While Martha stared open-mouthed at the remarkable sight a third man crawled from the chest. He had the same complexion as his fellows, but was short and fat.

70 All three were dressed in a curious manner. They wore short jackets of red velvet braided with gold, and knee breeches of sky-blue satin with silver buttons. Over their stockings were laced wide ribbons of red and yellow and blue, while their hats had broad brims with high, peaked crowns, from which fluttered yards of bright-colored ribbons.

75 "My! but you were heavy," exclaimed the fat one, when he had pulled down his velvet jacket and brushed the dust from his sky-blue breeches. "And you squeezed me all out of shape."

"It was unavoidable, Luigi," responded the thin man, lightly; "the lid of the chest pressed me down upon you. Yet I tender you my regrets."

80 "As for me," said the middle-sized man, carelessly rolling a cigarette and lighting it, "you must acknowledge I have been your nearest friend for years; so do not be disagreeable."

1. Why had Martha been left alone?
   - ⬭ a. She was disliked.
   - ⬭ b. Everyone had plans.
   - ⬭ c. Everyone had purposefully left her alone.
   - ⬭ d. She enjoyed the solitude.
   - ⬭ e. She was a recluse.

2. What was Emeline's key personality trait?
   - ⬭ a. patience
   - ⬭ b. tiredness
   - ⬭ c. hunger
   - ⬭ d. impatience
   - ⬭ e. rudeness

3. Which of the following best describes the big room under the roof?
   - ⬭ a. cold and miserable
   - ⬭ b. overheated
   - ⬭ c. agreeable
   - ⬭ d. spooky
   - ⬭ e. draughty and open

4. Which of the following is the best definition for 'wandering' in line 31?
   - ⬭ a. walking hurriedly
   - ⬭ b. running quickly
   - ⬭ c. travelling leisurely
   - ⬭ d. riding elephants
   - ⬭ e. asking questions

5. Which word best describes Uncle Walter's wooden chest?
   - ⬭ a. mysterious
   - ⬭ b. boring
   - ⬭ c. dangerous
   - ⬭ d. tatty
   - ⬭ e. incredulous

6. How could Martha tell what type of key was needed?
- a. She was a locksmith's daughter.
- b. She was a genius.
- c. The key was in the lock.
- d. There was a note telling her.
- e. The lock was large.

7. Which word is the best antonym for 'examine' in line 39?
- a. explore
- b. decipher
- c. inspect
- d. investigate
- e. ignore

8. How did Martha feel when the key fits the lock?
- a. worried
- b. impatient
- c. delighted
- d. bemused
- e. calm

9. 'Slowly and carefully a man unpacked himself from the chest...' (line 60)
   What are the words 'slowly' and 'carefully' examples of?

- a. adjectives
- b. adverbs
- c. verbs
- d. nouns
- e. conjunctions

10. What is likely reaction of the reader when the man steps out of the box?

- a. sad
- b. disappointed
- c. frustrated
- d. shocked
- e. indifferent

11. Which of these best describes the first man to step out of the box?
- a. tall and thin
- b. tall and fat
- c. round and plump
- d. small
- e. pale

12. How were the men dressed?
- a. in ill-fitting clothes
- b. like clowns
- c. like wizards
- d. like children
- e. in colourful clothes

13. What impact is the author intending to have on the reader during the men's dialogue?
- a. The reader should find it humorous.
- b. The reader should be offended.
- c. The reader should feel disappointed.
- d. The reader should be frustrated.
- e. The reader should be curious.

14. Who is the main character in this story?
- a. Luigi
- b. Martha
- c. Mrs. McFarland
- d. Emeline
- e. Sister Nell

15. Which of these statements is true?
- a. The extract is fictional.
- b. The extract is non-fictional.
- c. The extract is from a magazine.
- d. The extract belongs in the genre of romance.
- e. The extract is an example poetry.

BLANK PAGE

FIRST PAST THE POST® SERIES

11+ COMPREHENSIONS BOOK 1
CLASSIC LITERATURE

Tests 1 - 10

Answers

As you complete each question, remember that you can use the 11+ Peer-Compare System™ to see how well you performed in comparison to others who have taken this test.

You can register by visiting www.ElevenPlusExams.co.uk/FirstPastThePost to post your results anonymously and obtain the feedback.

Your unique 16 digit access code is:

PGT6-31P4-IWFQ-Q54N

Test 1 - Alice in Wonderland

Question	Answer	Source of Answer
1	D	Refer to lines 1-2: 'Alice was beginning to get very tired of sitting by her sister on the bank, and of having nothing to do.'
2	A	Refer to lines 2-3: '...it had no pictures or conversations in it, "and what is the use of a book," thought Alice, "without pictures or conversations?"'
3	C	Reader's personal judgement required. Refer to the referenced lines in order to help form an opinion as to how this passage should be described. The idea of a rabbit talking and carrying a watch is comical, so the best option is 'humorous'.
4	B	Reader's logical inference required. Refer to the description of the well in lines 19-30 to make a decision as to which of the given options provide the best description. As Alice takes a very long time to fall down the well and the sides were filled with cupboards and bookshelves, the best options are 'long' and 'magical'.
5	B	Reader's logical inference required. Use own knowledge to make a decision as to why Alice might be feeling disappointed. 'She would have liked to try some of it' is the most likely option as there is no other information given that suggests any of the other options are likely.
6	D	Knowledge of grammar required. A verb is a word that conveys an action. The action in this sentence is 'coming', so the verb is 'come'.
7	A	Knowledge of literary techniques required. 'Thump' is an example of an onomatopoeia. An onomatopoeia is a word that phonetically imitates the sound it is describing.
8	E	Reader's logical inference required. Refer to lines 30-35 to make a decision as to how Alice might be feeling. The sentence 'There was nothing else to do, so Alice soon began talking to herself.' gives the impression that Alice was bored.
9	C	Refer to line 14: '...burning with curiosity...'
10	D	Refer to lines 49-51: '...either the locks were too large, or the key was too small, but, at any rate, it would not open any of them.'
11	E	Reader's logical inference required. Refer to the quoted text within the context of the passage to make a decision as to whom Alice is speaking to. As there are no other characters around at this point, the reader can infer that Alice is speaking to herself.
12	D	Reader's personal judgement required. Refer to the quoted text within the context of the passage to help form an opinion as to how Alice might be feeling. As Alice has been portrayed as a likeable character, the image of her sitting down and crying evokes sympathy in the reader.
13	E	Knowledge of vocabulary required. The word 'seldom' means rarely. Therefore, the best option is 'not often'.
14	C	Reader's logical inference required. Refer to lines 92-93 to make a decision as to why Alice only eats a small amount of the cake. 'She has learned to be more cautious' is the most likely option as there is no evidence to imply that any of the other four are true.
15	B	Reader's personal judgement required. Look at the text as a whole, focussing on Alice's opinions, reactions and actions, to help form an opinion as to how old Alice might be. She is unlikely to be 5 years-old or younger as she forms articulate, advanced and considered decisions. Equally, she is unlikely to be older than 13 years-old as she is sufficiently curious to spend her day following a rabbit.

Test 2 - A Little Princess

Question	Answer	Source of Answer
1	B	Reader's personal judgement required. Refer to the description of the weather in lines 1-2 to help form an opinion as to which of the given options provides the best description. As words such as 'dark', 'winter' and 'fog' are used in line 1, the best option is 'gloomy'.
2	D	Refer to lines 1-2: '...in the streets of London...'
3	A	Knowledge of vocabulary required. The word 'blazed' means to burn or shine brightly. A synonym is a word that means the same, or nearly the same, as another word. Therefore, the option here that is the best synonym for 'blazed' is 'shone'.
4	B	Reader's logical inference required. Refer to the description of the way they were sitting in lines 5-6 to make a decision as to how they are likely to feel towards one another. As they are sitting so close to one another, the best option is that they love each other.
5	D	Refer to lines 12-13: 'She felt as if she had lived a long, long time.'
6	A	Knowledge of grammar required. An adjective is word that describes a noun or a pronoun. Therefore, the adjective here is 'big' as it is describing the ship.
7	C	Refer to line 22: 'She found this so puzzling that she moved closer to her father.'
8	B	Refer to line 23: '"Papa," she said in a low, mysterious little voice which was almost a whisper...'
9	C	Refer to lines 9-10: '...Sara Crewe was only seven.'
10	C	Refer to lines 31-32: 'Her mother had died when she was born, so she had never known or missed her.'
11	A	Refer to lines 43-44: 'During her short life only one thing had troubled her, and that thing was "the place" she was to be taken to someday.'
12	B	Refer to lines 44-45: 'The climate of India was very bad for children, and as soon as possible they were sent away from it...'
13	E	Reader's logical inference required. Refer to the phrases 'She did not care very much for other little girls...' (line 63) and 'She liked books more than anything else...' (lines 64-65) to infer that she must have been looking forward most to reading books at school.
14	D	Reader's personal judgement required. Refer to words and phrases such as 'lonely' (line 71) and '...he held her very closely in his arm...' (line 74) to help form an opinion as to how he might have been feeling. From these, it can be inferred that he was feeling sad at the prospect of leaving her, so the best option is 'melancholy'.
15	C	Knowledge of grammar required. 'A Little Princess' is a title. A title is the name of a creative work such as a book, published text, or programme.

Test 3 - A Modern Cinderella

Question	Answer	Source of Answer
1	B	Refer to line 1: 'Among green New England hills…'
2	D	Knowledge of vocabulary required. The word 'picturesque' means visually attractive in a charming way. Therefore, the best option is 'aesthetically ideal'.
3	D	Refer to line 3: '…a brook ran babbling through the orchard than encompassed it about…'
4	C	Refer to line 7: 'One summer morning…'
5	A	Reader's personal judgement required. Refer to the description of Nan in lines 12-13 to help form an opinion as to how Nan should be received. As she is described as 'blue-eyed' and 'soft-featured', it is likely that the reader is intended to think that she is likeable.
6	C	Refer to lines 25-26: '…for it's the only thing fit for me this hot weather.'
7	C	Knowledge of grammar required. A verb is a word that conveys an action. The action in this sentence is 'going', so the verb is 'went'.
8	C	Knowledge of vocabulary required. The word 'domestic' means existing inside a particular country or home. An antonym is a word that means the opposite of another word. Therefore, the option here that is the best antonym for 'domestic' is 'foreign'.
9	E	Reader's personal judgement required. Refer to the description of Nan in lines 52-59 to help form an opinion as to which of the given options provides the best description of her character. Words and phrases such as 'diligent' (line 52) and '…spirits would fail, though patience never' (line 59) imply that Nan is patient.
10	A	Reader's logical inference required. Refer to lines 53-59 to make a decision as to which of the given options best summarises the problem with the kitchen. Phrases such as '…rebellion broke out everywhere' (line 55) imply that it is messy and problem-filled.
11	B	Knowledge of literary techniques required. The quoted phrase is an example of a simile. A simile is a phrase that makes a comparison between two different things through a connective word such as 'like' or 'as'.
12	A	Reader's logical inference required. Refer to line 60 in the context of the passage in order to make a decision as to why Nan is 'growing hotter and wearier'. As the previous two paragraphs consist of descriptions of Nan's numerous tasks, it is likely that she is becoming hot and overworked.
13	C	Reader's personal judgement required. Refer to the referenced speech in lines 66-69 to help form an opinion as to what its main message is. By focussing on key phrases such as 'Help cometh from afar…' (line 67), it can be inferred that its main message is that 'Friends can help.'
14	B	Reader's personal judgement required. Refer to lines 70-76 to help form an opinion as to her response to John Lord. Words such as 'honest', 'kind' and 'helpful' in line 72, 'most welcome' in line 73 and 'grateful' in line 76 imply that she is grateful to see him.
15	E	Reader's personal judgement required. Look at the text as a whole to help form an opinion as to which character is the focus of the passage. As a great deal of the text is given over to describing Nan and her actions, it can be inferred that Nan is the main character in this story.

Test 4 - Black Beauty

Question	Answer	Source of Answer
1	C	Refer to line 1: 'The first place that I can well remember was a large pleasant meadow...'
2	C	Reader's logical inference required. Refer to specific sentences and phrases within the text such as '...I lived upon my mother's milk, as I could not eat grass.' (line 7) and '...we used to gallop...' (line 15) to make a decision as to what the narrator is likely to be. From these, it can be inferred that the narrator is a horse.
3	D	Reader's personal judgement required. Refer to the phrase '...I ran by her side, and at night I lay down close by her.' (line 8) to help form an opinion as to the nature of their relationship. This description gives the impression that the two horses were close.
4	D	Knowledge of vocabulary required. The word 'colt' means a young male horse. This can also be inferred from the sentence 'There were six young colts in the meadow besides me; they were older than I was; some were nearly as large as grown-up horses.' (lines 13-14), as this implies that colts grow up to become horses.
5	E	Refer to lines 16-17: 'Sometimes we had rather rough play, for they would frequently bite and kick as well as gallop.'
6	C	Reader's logical inference required. Refer to the section of his mother's speech in which she talks about the colts, lines 20-22, to make a decision as to what her message was. From the phrases '...they are cart-horse colts...' (line 21) and 'You have been well-bred...' (line 22), her message can be summarised as 'He is different to them.'
7	D	Reader's personal judgement required. Refer to lines 30-31 to help form an opinion as to why the master called her 'Pet'. As the 'master thought a great deal of her' (line 30) and 'Pet' is a name that is often used as an affectionate nickname, it can be inferred that the master was being affectionate.
8	A	Reader's personal judgement required. Refer to the quoted sentence in lines 39-40 and the paragraph in general to help form an opinion. Line 35: "..my mother loved him very much...she would neigh with joy.." so the best option is that she was fond of him and enjoyed pleasing him.
9	A	Reader's personal judgement required. Refer to lines 41-45 to help form an opinion as to how the narrator felt about Richard. The best option is that he found him annoying as Richard would throw stones and sticks that would hit and hurt the colts.
10	C	Reader's logical inference required. Refer to lines 47-53 to make a decision as to why the master gave Richard 'such a box on the ear' (lines 48-49). As the master said "bad boy! To chase the colts." (line 51), the best option is that he was angry with him.
11	A	Reader's personal judgement required. Refer to the description in lines 57-58 to help form an opinion as to what atmosphere is created. The phrase '...a light mist still hung over the woods...' (line 58) is most likely to create suspense.
12	D	Reader's logical inference required. Refer to lines 81-82 to make a decision as to what is likely to happen next. The phrase '...making straight for our meadow...' (line 82) implies that the dogs are likely to chase the hare into the horses' field.
13	C	Reader's personal judgement required. Refer to the last paragraph to help form an opinion as to which of the given options provides the best description of the ending. As the story is left in the middle of the action, the best option is 'exciting and unresolved'.
14	B	Knowledge of grammar required. As the pronoun 'I' and the possessive pronoun 'my' are used throughout the passage, it is written in 1st person narrative. The narrator also frequently gives opinions such as '...I think we were his favourites' (line 39).
15	B	Reader's personal judgement required. Look at the text as a whole to help form an opinion as to who are the intended readers. The language is likely to be too advanced for infants, yet the themes of the book are likely to be too immature for teenagers. Therefore, children are the intended readers.

Test 5 - Five Children and It

Question	Answer	Source of Answer
1	C	Knowledge of vocabulary required. A 'fly' is a horse and carriage. This can also be inferred from lines 2-3 'the children began to put their heads out of the carriage window'.
2	A	Reader's logical inference required. Refer to the quoted sentence in the context of the passage to make a decision as to how the children were feeling. It is most likely that they were feeling restless or impatient as none of the other options seem plausible.
3	B	Reader's logical inference required. Refer to the description of the route to the house in the first paragraph and to line 24-25 '...the house was deep in the country...' The word 'rural' means characteristic of the countryside and is therefore the best option.
4	E	Knowledge of vocabulary required. An 'orchard' is a place where fruit trees are grown. Therefore, 'e' is the best option.
5	B	Reader's logical inference required. Refer to the description of the mother's actions in lines 14-20 to make a decision as to which statement is true. As she 'was in no hurry' (line 15), it is most likely that she was the least excited.
6	A	Refer to lines 24-27: '...the house was deep in the country...and the children had been in London for two years...so the White House seemed to them a sort of Fairy Palace...'
7	E	Reader's logical inference required. Refer to lines 30-34 . The best option is 'There is nothing for them to do' as the narrator says that '...London has none of those nice things that children may play with...' (lines 32-33).
8	C	Refer to lines 40-44: '...children who live in towns are so extremely naughty...Children in the country are naughty sometimes, too, but that is for quite different reasons.'
9	A	Reader's logical inference required. Refer to lines 45-46 to make a decision as to why the children needed to be cleaned. As it says that 'The children had explored the gardens...' (line 45), it is likely that they are dirty for this reason, so option 'a' is the best.
10	D	Knowledge of literary techniques required. The quoted phrase is an example of a simile. A simile is a phrase that makes a comparison between two different things through a connective word such as 'like' or 'as'.
11	D	Refer to lines 53-54: '...Robert had found the broken swing and tumbled out of it and got a lump on his head...'
12	C	Reader's logical inference required. Refer to lines 58-61 to make a decision as to what the narrator is implying. As the narrator says that 'The best part of it all was that there were no rules...', he seems to be implying that the children disliked the rules in London.
13	A	Refer to lines 65-67: '...when the big chimneys were smoking...the valley looked as if it was filled with golden mist...'
14	B	Knowledge of vocabulary required. The word 'enchanted' means appearing to be under a spell. A synonym is a word that means the same, or nearly the same, as another word. Therefore, the option here that is the best synonym for 'enchanted' is 'magical'.
15	E	Reader's personal judgement required. Look at the passage as a whole to help form an opinion as to from whose perspective any opinions are given. As the pronoun 'I' is used throughout the passage, it is written in 1st person narrative. Therefore, any opinions are from the narrator's perspective, e.g. '...I am sure some tiresome person must have told you...' (lines 37-38).

Test 6 - How the Rhinoceros Got His Skin

Question	Answer	Source of Answer
1	C	Knowledge of vocabulary required. The word 'uninhabited' means without inhabitants. An antonym is a word that means the opposite of another word. Therefore, the option here that is the best antonym for 'uninhabited' is 'populated'.
2	E	Refer to lines 2-3: '...with nothing but his hat and his knife and a cooking-stove...'
3	D	Reader's personal judgement required. Refer to the description of the cake in lines 4-8 to help form an opinion as to what about it was peculiar. The only thing that stands out as strange is its size, being 'two feet across and three feet thick' (lines 5-6), which is too large for a normal cake.
4	D	Knowledge of literary techniques required. This phrase is descriptive. A descriptive phrase is one that assigns qualities to the object or person being described.
5	E	Reader's logical inference required. Refer to lines 14-16 to make a decision as to why the Man left the cake. As he climbed to the top of a tree, it is most likely that he was scared of the Rhinoceros and fled to safety.
6	B	Reader's personal judgement required. Refer to lines 17-18 to help form an opinion as to how the Rhinoceros might have felt. As he 'spiked that cake on the horn of his nose' (line 17) and 'went away, waving his tail' (line 18), it is most likely that he felt 'unapologetic' and 'smug'.
7	E	Knowledge of vocabulary required. The word 'recited' means repeated from memory. A synonym is a word that means the same, or nearly the same, as another word. Therefore, the option here that is the best synonym for 'recited' is 'performed'.
8	C	Knowledge of vocabulary required. The word 'dreadful' means extremely bad or serious.
9	E	Knowledge of literary techniques required. The song is best characterised as rhyming. A rhyming song or poem is one that is composed in rhyme so that certain lines end in corresponding sounds.
10	B	Reader's personal judgement required. Refer to the song in lines 23-25 to help form an opinion as to its main message. As the song is referring to the Rhinoceros: 'Whosoever takes a cake...' (line 23), the only likely option is option 'b': 'The Rhinoceros would regret his actions.'
11	A	Reader's logical inference required. Refer to the sentence '...the Man...found the skin, and he smiled one smile that ran all round his face two times.' (lines 35-36) to make a decision as to how the Man felt. From the description of his large smile, it is most likely that he felt ecstatic.
12	A	Reader's logical inference required. Refer to the phrase '(but he rubbed the buttons off)' in line 50 to make a decision as to why the Rhinoceros could not get rid of the cake-crumbs. As he had rubbed the buttons off his skin, he could no longer take it off, leaving the crumbs trapped inside.
13	A	Refer to lines 54-55: '...every rhinoceros has great folds in his skin and a very bad temper, all on account of the cake-crumbs inside.'
14	C	Reader's personal judgement required. As it is not true that rhinoceroses have cake-crumbs trapped inside their skins, this story is fictional or invented.
15	B	Knowledge of grammar required. Proper nouns, i.e. nouns that are specific or unique, are always capitalised. In this story, 'Man' and 'Rhinoceros' are acting as names for these characters and are therefore proper nouns. This means that they should be capitalised.

Test 7 - Little Women

Question	Answer	Source of Answer
1	D	Reader's logical inference required. Refer to line 1 to make a decision as to in which season this passage takes place. As line 1 makes is clear that it is Christmastime, the passage must take place in winter.
2	C	Reader's personal judgement required. Refer to their speech in lines 1-5 to help form an opinion as to which given option provides the best description. Words and phrases such as 'grumbled' (line 1), 'It's so dreadful...' (line 3) and 'I don't think it's fair...' (line 4) imply that they are complaining.
3	C	Reader's personal judgement required. 'contented' means 'satisfied'. Refer to lines 1-7, by comparing the sister's attitudes it can be inferred that Beth is the most contented as the others are complaining and therefore not satisfied.
4	D	Reader's logical inference required. Refer to line 11 to make a decision as to why their father is away. As the text says '...Father far away, where the fighting was.' (line 11), it can be inferred that their father is a soldier.
5	A	Knowledge of vocabulary required. The word 'regretfully' means feeling sad or disappointed. A synonym is a word that means the same, or nearly the same, as another word. The best option for 'regretfully' is 'sorrowfully', and it is the only word that fits in the sentence.
6	E	Refer to lines 14-16: '...she thinks we ought not to spend money for pleasure, when our men are suffering so in that army. We can't do much, but we can make our little sacrifices...'
7	E	Reader's logical inference required. Refer to line 21-22 to make a decision as to what 'Undine and Sintran' is. Jo says she wants to buy it and she is then described as a 'bookworm' (line 22), therefore it can be inferred that 'Undine and Sintran' is most likely to be a book.
8	A	Reader's logical inference required. Refer to the descriptions of what each sister does in lines 31-42 to make a decision as to which sister is the youngest. As all of the sisters describe jobs, but Amy describes going to school, it can be inferred that Amy is the youngest.
9	B	Knowledge of vocabulary required. The word 'impertinent' means not showing proper respect. An antonym is a word that means the opposite of another word. Therefore, the option here that is the best antonym for 'impertinent' is 'polite'.
10	D	Reader's logical inference required. Refer to the sentence "Don't you wish we had the money Papa lost when we were little...?" (lines 49-50) to make a decision as to which statement is true. This sentence implies that the family used to have more money, so the best option is 'd'.
11	C	Knowledge of vocabulary required. The word 'reproving' means reprimanding or telling off. Therefore, the best option to explain the quoted phrase is 'She looks at her as if she wants to tell her off.'
12	C	Reader's personal judgement required. Refer to lines 59-61 to help form an opinion as to which of the given options provides the best description of Jo. The sentences '"It's so boyish!" "That's why I do it."' imply that Jo deliberately chooses to appear 'boyish' rather than 'feminine'.
13	D	Reader's personal judgement required. Look at the passage as a whole to help form an opinion as to what its focus is. As the majority of the text consists of descriptions of the sisters and their interactions, 'the sisters and how they interact' must be the focus.
14	E	Reader's personal judgment required. Look at the text as a whole to help form an opinion as to what its moral is. As there does not seem to be an overriding message, and the other four options are definitely not advocated in the text, 'There was no moral' is the best option.
15	C	Reader's personal judgement required. Look at the text as a whole to help form an opinion as to what type of text it is likely to come from. As the story is not factual, it must have come from 'a fictitious novel'. However, it does not have any scientific themes, so option 'c' is the best option.

Test 8 - Oliver Twist

Question	Answer	Source of Answer
1	B	Reader's logical inference required. Refer to lines 3-5 to make a decision as to why the clothes needed to be taken in. As the clothes 'fluttered loosely on their wasted, shrunken forms' (line 4), it can be inferred that the clothes were too big for the skinny children.
2	C	Refer to lines 8-9: '...the master...assisted by one or two women, ladled the gruel...'
3	E	Refer to line 10: '...each boy had one porringer, and no more...'
4	D	Refer to lines 13-14: 'The bowls never wanted washing. They boys polished them with their spoons till they shone again...'
5	B	Refer to lines 22-25: '...one boy, who...hadn't been used to that sort of thing...hinted darkly to his companions, that unless he had another basin of gruel per diem, he was afraid he might some night happen to eat the boy who slept next him...'
6	A	Knowledge of vocabulary required. A 'council' is a body of people that meets for consultation or advice. Therefore, option 'a' is the best.
7	C	Refer to lines 32-33: '...the gruel was served out; and a long grace was said over the short commons...'
8	C	Refer to line 37: '...somewhat alarmed at his own temerity:' 'temerity' means 'brave'.
9	C	Reader's personal judgement required. Refer to lines 39-43 in the context of the rest of the passage to help form an opinion as to why the master replied in a faint voice. The phrase 'He gazed in stupefied astonishment...' (lines 39-40) implies that he was shocked.
10	A	Refer to lines 59-63: 'Oliver was ordered into instant confinement; and a bill was next morning pasted on the outside of the gate, offering a reward of five pounds to anybody who would take Oliver Twist off the hands of the parish. In other words, five pounds and Oliver Twist were offered to any man or woman who wanted an apprentice...'
11	E	Reader's personal judgement required. Refer to lines 51-54 to help form an opinion as to why the adults reacted in this way. As Mr. Limbkins says "For more!...after he had eaten the supper allotted by the dietary?", the most likely options are 1 and 2.
12	D	Reader's personal judgement required. Look at the text as a whole to form an opinion as to which character is intended to be the reader's favourite. As the focus of the passage is what happens to Oliver, it is most likely that he is intended to be the reader's favourite.
13	D	Knowledge of vocabulary required. The word 'consequence' means a result or effect. An antonym is a word that means the opposite of another word. Therefore, the option here that is the best antonym for 'consequence' is 'cause'.
14	B	Knowledge of vocabulary required. The word 'stupefied' means shocked or unable to think properly.
15	A	Knowledge of grammar required. The quoted sentence is an example of a request. A request is an act of asking politely for something.

Test 9 - Peter Pan

Question	Answer	Source of Answer
1	C	Refer to lines 4-5: '...Wendy's light blinked and gave such a yawn that the other two yawned also...'
2	A	Refer to lines 15-16: 'He had carried Tinker Bell part of the way, and his hand was still messy with the fairy dust.'
3	E	Reader's logical inference required. Refer to lines 22-24 to make a decision as to why Peter could understand Tinker Bell. As it is stated in the text that 'if you were to hear it you would know that you had heard it once before' (lines 23-24), it can be inferred that Peter had heard the fairy language many times before.
4	C	Reader's logical inference required. Refer to lines 25-29 to make a decision as to how Peter felt when he found his shadow. It can be inferred from the word 'delight' (line 28) and that fact that he forgot about Tinker Bell that he felt 'triumphant'.
5	A	Refer to lines 32-34: '...when they did not he was appalled. He tried to stick it on with soap from the bathroom, but that also failed. A shudder passed through Peter, and he sat on the floor and cried.'
6	B	Refer to lines 35-36: 'She was not alarmed to see a stranger crying on the nursery floor; she was only pleasantly interested.'
7	B	Knowledge of vocabulary required. The word 'courteously' means respectfully or considerately. A synonym is a word that means the same, or nearly the same, as another word. Therefore, the option here that is the best synonym for 'courteously' is 'politely'.
8	E	Reader's logical inference required. Refer to lines 42-47 to make a decision as to why Wendy asks "Is that all?" (line 47). The phrase '...it did seem a comparatively short name' (lines 45-46) implies that Wendy was surprised that his name was shorter than hers.
9	B	Reader's logical inference required. Refer to lines 55-56 to make a decision as to how Peter felt. As 'Peter had a sinking.' (line 55), it is most likely that he felt embarrassed.
10	D	Knowledge of vocabulary required. The word 'hostess' means 'a woman who receives and entertains guests'.
11	B	Refer to lines 63-64: '...he had not the slightest desire to have one. He thought them very over-rated persons.'
12	C	Knowledge of grammar required. The quoted sentence is an example of an exclamation. An exclamation is a word or phrase used to express an emotion.
13	B	Reader's personal judgement required. Refer to lines 81-83 in the context of the passage to help form an opinion as to why Wendy refers to Peter in this way. In line 75-76 it is said that Wendy spoke 'patronisingly' and in line 82-83 she 'got out her...[sewing bag]' , the most likely options are 1 and 4.
14	E	Knowledge of literary techniques required. The quoted sentence is an example of irony. Irony is the use of language to convey a different or opposite meaning to the words actually used.
15	A	Reader's personal judgement required. Look at the test as a whole to help form an opinion as to what genre of book the extract is from. As the text includes mentions of fairies and fairy dust, it is most likely to be from a fantasy book.

Test 10 - The Box of Robbers

Question	Answer	Source of Answer
1	B	Refer to lines 1-2: 'No one intended to leave Martha alone that afternoon, but it happened that everyone was called away...'
2	D	Refer to line 7: '...Emeline had a restless nature.'
3	C	Reader's personal judgement required. Refer to the description of the room in lines 20-21 to help form an opinion as to which of the given options provides the best description. The words 'warm' and 'pleasant' in line 21 imply that the best option is 'agreeable'.
4	C	Knowledge of vocabulary required. The word 'wandering' means travelling aimlessly from place to place. Therefore, the best option is 'travelling leisurely'.
5	A	Reader's personal judgement required. Refer to the description of the chest and its origins in lines 27-33 to help form an opinion as to which of the given options provides the best description. As 'there was no key to it' (lines 29-30) and it was 'to remain unopened' (line 30), the best option is 'mysterious'.
6	E	Reader's logical inference required. Refer to lines 39-40 to make a decision as to how she knew what type of key was needed. As 'she stooped to examine the lock' (line 39), it is most likely that she came to her conclusion because 'the lock was large'.
7	E	Knowledge of vocabulary required. The word 'examine' means to inspect thoroughly. An antonym is a word that means the opposite of another word. Therefore, the option here that is the best antonym for 'examine' is 'ignore'.
8	C	Reader's logical inference required. Refer to lines 54-56 to make a decision as to how Martha felt. As she uttered 'a cry of joy' (line 55), it is most likely that she felt 'delighted'.
9	B	Knowledge of grammar required. The words 'slowly' and 'carefully' (line 60) are examples of adverbs. An adverb is a word that describes a verb, adjective or other adverb.
10	D	Reader's personal judgement required. Refer to lines 60-62 and think about how you felt as you read these lines to help form an opinion as to how the reader should feel. The most likely option here is 'shocked' as the appearance of the man is unexpected.
11	A	Refer to line 63: 'He was tall and thin...'
12	E	Refer to lines 70-74: '...jackets of red velvet braided with gold, and knee breeches of sky-blue satin with silver buttons...ribbons of red and yellow and blue...bright-colored ribbons.'
13	A	Reader's personal judgement required. Refer to lines 75-82 and think about how you felt as you read these lines to help form an opinion as to how the reader should feel. The most likely option is that 'the reader should find it humorous', as the other options can be eliminated.
14	B	Reader's personal judgement required. Look at the text as a whole to help form an opinion as to which character is the focus of the passage. As a great deal of the text is given over to describing Martha's actions, it can be inferred that Martha is the main character in this story.
15	A	Reader's personal judgement required. Look at the text as a whole to help form an opinion as to what genre it falls into. As the story is not factual, options 'b' and 'c' are definitely not correct. Furthermore, it does not contain any romance and it is not structured like a poem. Therefore, option 'a' is the best option.

BLANK PAGE